Slow-Wave Propagation in Plasma Waveguides

A. W. TRIVELPIECE

San Francisco Press, Inc.

255 12th Street, San Francisco, California

To Shirley

table of contents

preface, vii

author's preface, viii

1 introduction, 1

2 plasmaguide modes in an infinite axial magnetic field, 8

Definition of plasma, *8*; The plasma-filled waveguide, *9*; Power flow, *15*; Simple physical explanation for plasmaguide modes, *16*; Electromechanical nature of the plasmaguide waves, *18*; Review of the features of plasmaguide propagation for an infinite axial magnetic field, *19*

3 plasmaguide modes for finite dc magnetic fields, 20

Dielectric constant of a plasma in a dc magnetic field, *20*; Plasma column in waveguide, *22*; Properties of a plasma-filled waveguide, *26*; Ac magnetic fields from quasistatic approximation, *32*; Power flow for plasma-filled waveguide, *34*; Properties of a plasma column in a waveguide, *35*; Faraday rotation, *40*; Plasmaguide mode for magnetic field transverse to direction of propagation, *45*; Review of the properties of plasmaguide waves in finite magnetic fields, *50*

4 plasmaguide waves for zero dc magnetic field, 52

Simple method for obtaining low-frequency phase velocities of plasma waves, *57*; Plasmaguide surface waves of one angular variation, *59*; Equivalent electrical transmission line for surface waves, *62*; Backward surface waves on a plasma column, *63*; The effect of radial charge density variation on the plasma-column surface waves, *69*; Power flow associated with surface waves on a plasma column, *78*; Review of the features of plasmaguide propagation for zero dc magnetic field, *81*

5 interaction of an electron beam with the plasmaguide modes, 83

Field analysis of electron-beam plasmaguide interaction, *84*; Approximate analysis of electron-beam plasmaguide interaction, *89*; Energy conservation in plasmaguide waves, *97*; Attenuation of plasmaguide waves, *100*

6 relation of plasmaguide modes to space-charge waves on drifting electron beams, 102

7 slow-wave propagation in ferrite waveguides, 108

Ferrite rod in a cylindrical waveguide, *108*; Ferrite-filled waveguide in finite axial dc magnetic field, *113*

8 experimental results, 116

Description of experiment, *116*; Plasma column in a cylindrical waveguide: Finite magnetic field, *120*; Plasma column in a cylindrical waveguide: Zero magnetic field, *125*; Plasma diagnostics, *127*

9 summary and conclusions, 131

appendix I: one-dimensional space-charge waves, 136

appendix II: admittance transformation, 138

appendix III: space charge waves in cylindrical plasma columns, 140

references, 164

preface

WORKERS IN plasma research and in the growing
plasma industry will welcome the appearance of an
updated, complete version of this pioneering
work, not previously available in book form,
reinforced by the additional results presented in
a journal article. The demand for reprints of
that article and of the original mimeographed
report (both now out of print) remains lively.

It is not too much to say that this is the
definitive work on the propagation of plasma
waves in finite configurations, as well as one of
the first experimental demonstrations of such
propagation. The eminently successful way in
which the author has related theory to experiment
opens the way for the determination of the properties of low-temperature plasmas, a contribution
to the field of plasma diagnostics that is not
only of lasting scientific but also of considerable
pedagogical interest. This treatment of waves in
low-temperature bounded plasmas also gives considerable insight into the characteristics of
waves in hot bounded plasmas, a subject of great
current interest.

Those of us who have urged the author to
make this work more generally available were
prompted in part by our finding that some of the
results keep turning up as new "discoveries" in
current literature.

ROY W. GOULD

Pasadena, California, 1967

author's preface

THIS MONOGRAPH has been published in response to
continued requests for copies of a technical report of the same name issued in May 1958 at the
California Institute of Technology under the terms
of a contract with the Office of Naval Research.
That report, which was based on my Ph.D. thesis,
was the basis for a paper that contained additional
results and was published in the Journal of Applied
Physics. This paper, co-authored with R. W. Gould,
is reproduced in Appendix III.

The other reason for producing this monograph
stems from the increased intensity of instructional
laboratory work in plasma physics, both at the
graduate and the undergraduate level, at many
institutions of higher learning, and the need for
simple experiments illustrating plasma properties.
The present work constitutes a useful reference for
anyone setting up a laboratory course involving
experiments demonstrating plasma dielectric properties and plasma wave propagation characteristics.
Although some of the material (presented more
formally) has found its way into various textbooks,
the method of analysis and the development of the
ideas make this work a good introduction to the
subject.

The original acknowledgment is reproduced
below:

I wish particularly to thank Profs. Roy W.
Gould and Lester M. Field for their advice,
interest, and encouragement throughout this
investigation. Mr. Gary Boyd is thanked for
his advice on construction of the experimental
plasma tubes. Thanks are also extended to
Prof. Joel Franklin and Mr. Ken Hebert, who
prepared the computer programs; to Mr. Tom

Hays, who assisted in the computations; and to Mr. Pete Carpenter, Mr. Eric Gelin, and Mr. Bob Stratton, who constructed the experimental equipment.

In addition, I acknowledge the many editorial improvements in this work resulting from suggestions made by Prof. C. Süsskind.

A. W. T.

College Park, Maryland, 1967

introduction

ONE OF THE FUNDAMENTAL limitations in the generation of higher microwave frequencies with conventional negative-grid vacuum tubes comes from the
fact that an electron may spend an appreciable
fraction of a cycle in the cathode-grid region.
To overcome the deleterious effects of such a
condition,[1] the Heils[2] and the Varian brothers[3]
proposed a device (the klystron) that utilizes a
drifting electron beam to produce dense current
bunches, which are passed through a cavity resonator where the rf energy can be extracted. Webster made the first satisfactory analysis of a
klystron using a kinematic or bunching theory.[4]
He assumed that a single-velocity electron beam
passes through a narrow-gap cavity resonator,
which perturbs the average velocity of the electrons in the beam, sinusoidally in time. The
electrons which were decelerated by the cavity
fields are overtaken by electrons which were ac-
celerated by the cavity fields, but which left
the cavity at a slightly later time. This process results in dense bunches of electrons at
some distance along the beam centered about the
electron that passed through the cavity when the
cavity fields were changing from decelerating to
accelerating. The operating characteristics of
the klystron can then be determined by investigating the problem of passing these dense current
bunches through a narrow-gap cavity resonator
similar to the one used to perturb the electron
velocities. Although the kinematic theory satis-
factorily accounts for klystron operation in most
cases, it is by no means complete, since the mu-
tual repulsion (space-charge) forces between
electrons have been neglected.

A more general theory including space charge was worked out by Hahn[5] and by Ramo.[6] One of the problems they considered was that of a drifting, ion-neutralized, cylindrical electron beam in an infinite axial magnetic field. They found in general that two space-charge waves are associated with the drifting motion of an electron beam. One of these space-charge waves has a phase velocity slightly greater than the average velocity of the electron beam (fast space-charge wave) and the other has a phase velocity which is, in the case of a one-dimensional electron beam, smaller by an equal amount than the average electron beam velocity (slow space-charge wave). The propagation equation for these space-charge waves in a one-dimensional electron beam is[*]

$$\omega_p^2 - (\omega - \beta u_{0z})^2 = 0 \qquad (I.1)$$

where $\omega_p^2 = -\rho_0 e/\epsilon_0 m$ is the electron plasma frequency, u_{0z} is the average electron beam velocity, and all quantities are assumed to have exp $j(\omega t - \beta z)$ dependence. The solutions of this equation are

$$\beta = \frac{\omega + \omega_p}{u_{0z}} \qquad (I.2)$$

$$\beta = \frac{\omega - \omega_p}{u_{0z}} \qquad (I.3)$$

These traveling-wave solutions have different phase velocities $(v_{ph} = \omega/\beta)$

_____

[*]A simple derivation is given in Appendix I.

$$v_{ph} = \frac{\omega}{\omega - \omega_p} u_{0z} \qquad \text{(fast space-charge} \qquad \text{(I.4)}$$
$$\text{wave)}$$

$$v_{ph} = \frac{\omega}{\omega + \omega_p} u_{0z} \qquad \text{(slow space-charge} \qquad \text{(I.5)}$$
$$\text{wave)}$$

but have the same group velocity (v_g = $d\omega/d\beta$)

$$v_g = u_{0z} \qquad\qquad\qquad \text{(I.6)}$$

The group velocity represents the rate of energy transfer, and as can be seen from Eq. (I.6), a stationary (u_{0z} = 0), one-dimensional electron beam does not propagate space-charge disturbances. These space-charge waves are just the natural plasma oscillations bodily transported at the average drift velocity of the plasma, so that an observer moving with the drift velocity would see a plasma resonance that does not depend on the wavelength of the disturbance. As will be shown, however, an average velocity of the electron beam is not essential to the propagation of space-charge disturbances when the electron beam has finite transverse configuration. The propagation equations derived by Hahn[5] and Ramo[6] predict this behavior; however, their interest was confined to the drifting-electron-beam solutions and the possibility of propagation along a stationary electron beam was not considered.

Rigrod and Lewis[7] considered the somewhat more difficult problem of an electron beam formed in a region of zero dc axial magnetic field injected into a region of nonzero axial magnetic field, the magnetic field being chosen to be of the proper value to produce an inward force on the electrons that just cancels the outward space-charge force and the centrifugal force on the electrons. This type of focusing is known as

Brillouin flow.[8]   They found two types of space-
charge-wave propagation. One of these types of
propagation involves a perturbation in the average
charge density; the other type involves a rippling
of the surface of the electron beam with no perturbation of the average charge density.

Brewer[9] and Labus[10] have recently treated
the even more difficult problem of space-charge-
wave propagation on an electron beam in an axial
dc magnetic field of arbitrary strength. Such an
analysis was appropriate since the magnetic fields
available in the laboratory are smaller than the
infinite value assumed by Hahn and Ramo, but
greater than the value necessary to produce
Brillouin flow.

Although none of these later investigators
considered the problem of space-charge-wave propagation in the absence of any drifting motion of
the electron beam, the problem of electromagnetic-
wave propagation in waveguides filled with stationary ion-neutralized plasmas in arbitrary
axial magnetic fields has received considerable
attention. Suhl and Walker,[11] Gamo,[12] VanTrier,[13]
and others have examined how the well-known electromagnetic modes of propagation in a waveguide
are modified by the introduction of a plasma into
the waveguide system. In particular, they examined how the cutoff frequencies of the various
modes of propagation that exist in the system are
perturbed by the presence of the plasma and how
the plane of polarization of the angularly dependent modes is rotated (Faraday rotation) as a
function of distance along the waveguide. They
found in general that the mode cutoff frequencies
are increased by the presence of the plasma and
that the combined presence of plasma and axial
magnetic field results in Faraday rotation. They
did not find, however, that slow-wave space-charge
modes of propagation exist analogous to those on a
drifting beam at frequencies which are usually

well below the cutoff frequency for the empty
waveguide system (actually below the plasma frequency for the plasma-filled waveguide when the
dc magnetic field is infinite).

One of the useful applications of the space-
charge-wave theory described earlier is that of
calculating the amount of noise power contributed
to the output of a klystron or traveling-wave
tube[14] by the electron beam in order to determine
what combination of parameters is required to
make this noise power a minimum.[15-18] At the
cathode or potential minimum of an electron gun
or diode producing an electron beam, there are
two sources of noise[19] that serve as the boundary
conditions for the two space-charge waves. These
noise disturbances propagate along the electron
beam according to the space-charge-wave theory,
ultimately appearing at the output of the amplifier that utilizes the electron beam with some
finite value. The extent to which this noise
power can be minimized determines the ultimate
sensitivity or noise figure* of the amplifier. In
most microwave devices using electron beams, the
plasma frequency is of the order of hundreds of
megacycles and the operating frequency is of the
order of thousands of megacycles.

This condition permits the effects of finite
configuration on space-charge-wave propagation to
be included as a slight modification to the one-
dimensional space-charge-wave theory. The modification involves using a plasma frequency smaller
than that appropriate to the average charge density. This reduced plasma frequency is, just as
with the one-dimensional electron beam, the plasma
oscillation as seen by an observer moving with the

---

*The sum of the amplified thermal noise assoc-
iated with the input impedance and the noise power
from the electron beam divided by the amplified
thermal noise.

electron beam. The plasma oscillation frequency
is reduced because some of the electric field now
terminates on the charges induced in the conducting
wall (assuming the electron beam is contained in a
conducting cylinder), thereby reducing the longitudinal restoring force. The amount by which the
plasma frequency is reduced depends on both the
wavelength of the disturbance and the transverse
configuration. For short-wavelength disturbances,
the fields do not extend very far outside the electron beam, and if the conducting wall is far re-
moved, there is only a slight reduction in the
plasma frequency. For long-wavelength disturbances,
the fields do extend from the plasma and the reduction in plasma frequency is quite significant;
in fact, the plasma frequency is reduced to zero
for disturbances of infinite wavelength. Thus the
propagation constants for space-charge waves in a
finite configuration can be expressed

$$\beta = \frac{\omega \pm R\omega_p}{u_{0z}} \qquad (I.7)$$

where the reduction factor R is in this case a
function of the configuration, beam velocity, and
operating frequency. In the case of traveling-
wave amplifiers operating at low frequencies,
however, it is possible to realize operating conditions where the plasma frequency near the potential minimum may exceed the operating frequency.
In the course of investigating the consequences of
this situation on the propagation of noise disturbances near the potential minimum,[20] it became
evident that there were associated with very slowly
moving and stationary electron beams, i.e., with
modes of propagation other than the slow and fast
space-charge waves.[21] Presumably these additional
modes of propagation are of significance in determining how noise disturbances propagate from the

potential minimum and may have a marked influence
on the minimum noise figure of a traveling-wave
tube operating in this region. However, these
additional modes of propagation are of sufficient
interest to warrant investigation for their own
sake, and the present contribution is primarily
concerned with a study of their properties.
Smullin and Chorney have also independently reported the existence of these modes of
propagation.[22]

It is our purpose to investigate the propagation of space-charge-wave disturbances in stationary ion-neutralized plasmas of finite
configuration, to describe the experimental
measurements made to verify their existence, and
to demonstrate their relation to space-charge
waves on moving electron beams.

plasmaguide modes in an infinite axial magnetic field

ALL OF THE "PLASMAGUIDE"* modes of propagation treated below are slow waves, i.e., the phase velocity of the waves is much smaller than the velocity of light. The properties of these slow-wave modes can be adequately described by an approximate analysis that neglects the ac magnetic fields (quasi-static approximation); however, it is appropriate to examine at least one of these modes of propagation including the ac magnetic field. For small signals, the case of the plasma-filled guide in an infinite axial dc magnetic field provides an example that can be treated by the complete Maxwell equations without becoming unduly complicated. This treatment can be then compared with the approximate analysis for the same solution.

DEFINITION OF PLASMA. The term plasma will be used in this paper to denote a partially ionized gas which, in the absence of disturbances, is electrically neutral. Unless otherwise noted, it will be assumed for this plasma that the ions are stationary, that the electrons have no thermal or random velocities and suffer no collisions, and that the neutral gas molecules play no role at all. Ionization and recombination will also be neglected. Such a plasma as described above might be termed an <u>ideal electron plasma</u>.

---

*The term "plasmaguide" will be used to denote any of the slow-wave modes on a nondrifting, ion-neutralized, plasma column.

THE PLASMA-FILLED WAVEGUIDE. Consider now a perfectly conducting cylindrical waveguide completely filled with an <u>ideal electron plasma</u> and let there be an infinite axial magnetic field, $B_0 = \infty$.*

To study the propagation of waves in this system, the Maxwell equations will be used,

$$\nabla \times \underline{E} = -\partial \underline{B}/\partial t \quad \text{(II.1)} \qquad \nabla \cdot \underline{B} = 0 \quad \text{(II.4)}$$

$$\nabla \times \underline{H} = \underline{J} + \partial \underline{D}/\partial t \quad \text{(II.2)} \qquad \underline{B} = \mu \underline{H} \quad \text{(II.5)}$$

$$\nabla \cdot \underline{D} = \rho \quad \text{(II.3)} \qquad \underline{D} = \epsilon \underline{E} \quad \text{(II.6)}$$

along with the equation of motion,

$$\frac{\partial \underline{v}}{\partial t} + (\underline{v} \cdot \nabla)\underline{v} = -\frac{e}{m}\underline{E} - \frac{e}{m}\underline{v} \times \underline{B} \quad \text{(II.7)}$$

and the equation of continuity,

$$\nabla \cdot \underline{J} = -\partial \rho/\partial t \quad \text{(II.8)}$$

where the convection current density $\underline{J} = \rho\underline{v}$ is assumed to be due to the electrons only and the symbol "e" is used to denote the magnitude of the electronic charge only.

We assume that all quantities have an average value plus a small harmonic time-dependent perturbation,

$$\underline{F}(r,t) = \underline{F}_0(r) + \underline{F}_1(r)e^{j\omega t} \quad \text{(II.9)}$$

and are wave-like in nature,

---

*Subscripts zero and one will be used to denote dc and ac quantities respectively.

$$\underline{F}_1(x,y,z) = \underline{F}_1(x,y)e^{-\Gamma z} \qquad (II.10)$$

where Γ is the complex propagation constant

$$\Gamma = \alpha + j\beta \qquad (II.11)$$

These assumptions allow Eqs. (II.1) and (II.2) to be written in component form for cylindrical coordinates in terms of the ac quantities, as follows:

$$\frac{1}{r}\frac{\partial E_{1z}}{\partial \theta} + \Gamma E_{1\theta} = -j\omega\mu_0 H_{1r} \qquad (II.12)$$

$$-\Gamma E_{1r} - \frac{\partial E_{1z}}{\partial r} = -j\omega\mu_0 H_{1\theta} \qquad (II.13)$$

$$\frac{1}{r}\frac{\partial}{\partial r}(rE_{1\theta}) - \frac{1}{r}\frac{\partial E_{1r}}{\partial \theta} = -j\omega\mu_0 H_{1z} \qquad (II.14)$$

$$\frac{1}{r}\frac{\partial H_{1z}}{\partial \theta} + \Gamma H_{1\theta} = j\omega\epsilon_0 E_{1r} \qquad (II.15)$$

$$-\Gamma H_{1r} - \frac{\partial H_{1z}}{\partial r} = j\omega\epsilon_0 E_{1\theta} \qquad (II.16)$$

$$\frac{1}{r}\frac{\partial}{\partial r}(rH_{1\theta}) - \frac{1}{r}\frac{\partial H_{1r}}{\partial \theta} = j\omega\epsilon_0 E_{1z} + J_{1z} \qquad (II.17)$$

where J_{1r} and $J_{1\theta}$ have been set equal to zero since the electrons cannot move in the r or θ directions. The above equations, (II.12-17), can be combined to give the field components E_{1r}, $E_{1\theta}$, H_{1r}, $H_{1\theta}$, in terms of E_{1z} and H_{1z} only:

$$E_{1r} = -\frac{1}{(\Gamma^2 + k^2)} \left(\Gamma \frac{\partial E_{1z}}{\partial r} + \frac{j\omega\mu_0}{r} \frac{\partial H_{1z}}{\partial \theta} \right) \quad (II.18)$$

$$E_{1\theta} = \frac{1}{(\Gamma^2 + k^2)} \left(-\frac{\Gamma}{r} \frac{\partial E_{1z}}{\partial \theta} + j\omega\mu_0 \frac{\partial H_{1z}}{\partial r} \right) (II.19)$$

$$H_{1r} = \frac{1}{(\Gamma^2 + k^2)} \left(\frac{j\omega\epsilon_0}{r} \frac{\partial E_{1z}}{\partial \theta} - \Gamma \frac{\partial H_{1z}}{\partial r} \right) \quad (II.20)$$

$$H_{1\theta} = \frac{-1}{(\Gamma^2 + k^2)} \left(j\omega\epsilon_0 \frac{\partial E_{1z}}{\partial r} + \frac{1}{r} \frac{\partial H_{1z}}{\partial \theta} \right) \quad (II.21)$$

where $k^2 = \omega^2\mu_0\epsilon_0$ is the free-space wave number. All field components can be thus derived from E_{1z} and H_{1z}. The differential equations that E_{1z} and H_{1z} must satisfy are

$$\nabla_T^2 E_{1z} + \Gamma^2 E_{1z} + k^2 E_{1z} = j\omega\mu_0 J_{1z} - \Gamma \rho_1/\epsilon_0$$

$$\text{(II.22)}$$

$$\nabla_T^2 H_{1z} + (\Gamma^2 + k^2) H_{1z} = 0 \qquad \text{(II.23)}$$

where the symbol Γ_T^2 denotes the transverse Laplacian, which for cylindrical coordinates is

$$\nabla_T^2 = \frac{1}{r} \frac{\partial}{\partial r} \left(r \frac{\partial}{\partial r} \right) + \frac{1}{r^2} \frac{\partial^2}{\partial \theta^2} \qquad (II.24)$$

Since the differential equation for H_{1z} does not depend on the presence of the electrons it can be concluded that the H-modes, i.e., the modes that can be derived from H_{1z} only, are not affected by

the electrons. This result is also obtainable
from physical considerations by noting that the
infinite axial magnetic field constrains the electrons to z motion only and the H modes have no
electric field component along the z coordinate to
act on the electrons. The H-mode solutions are
therefore not of interest in this analysis.

The E modes, i.e., the modes that can be derived from E_{1z} only, <u>are</u> influenced by the presence of the electrons. The solutions of the
differential equation (II.22) together with the
appropriate boundary conditions leads to the propagation equation for the plasmaguide modes. This
analysis is identical with the derivation for the
ordinary Hahn-Ramo space-charge waves,[5,6] which are
associated with the drifting motion of an electron
beam; however, it will be shown that even in the
absence of any drift motion of the plasma, propagation of an electromechanical nature can exist
down at frequencies below the E-mode cutoff frequency and the plasma frequency.

Neglecting the forces on the electrons due
to the ac magnetic fields and eliminating the ac
convection current density and ac charge density
from (II.22) by means of the equations of motion
(II.7) and of continuity (II.8) leads to

$$\left[\nabla_T^2 + (\Gamma^2 + k^2)\left(1 - \frac{\omega_p^2}{\omega^2}\right) \right] E_{1z} = 0 \qquad (II.25)$$

where $\omega_p^2 = -\rho_0 e/\epsilon_0 m$ is the electron plasma frequency. The differential equation in E_{1z} is a
linear approximation, in that products and higher-
order combinations of the ac perturbation quantities have been neglected. If we define

$$T^2 \equiv (\Gamma^2 + k^2)\left(1 - \frac{\omega_p^2}{\omega^2}\right) \qquad \text{(II.26)}$$

the solutions of (II.25) are

$$E_{1z} = E_{1z}(0)J_n(Tr) \qquad \text{(II.27)}$$

where $e^{jn\theta}$ angular dependence has been assumed and the second solution (which is not finite at the origin) has been omitted.

Since the plasma completely fills the conducting waveguide, application of the appropriate boundary condition (that the tangential electric field must vanish on the waveguide surface) leads to

$$J_n(Ta) = 0 \qquad Ta = p_{n\nu} \qquad \text{(II.28)}$$

where a is the waveguide radius and $p_{n\nu}$ is the νth root of the nth-order Bessel function of the first kind. We solve for the propagation constant in (II.26) by using (II.28):

$$\Gamma^2 = -\beta^2 = -k^2 + \frac{(p_{n\nu}/a)^2}{1 - (\omega_p/\omega)^2} \qquad \text{(II.29)}$$

For propagating waves, $\alpha = 0$ and $\Gamma^2 = -\beta^2$, where $\beta^2 > 0$. Setting Γ^2 equal to zero and solving for the cutoff frequency leads to the familiar result that the E-mode cutoff frequency for a plasma-filled guide is equal to the cutoff frequency for the empty guide increased by the plasma frequency

$$\omega_{c0}^2 = T^2 c^2 + \omega_p^2 \qquad \text{(II.30)}$$

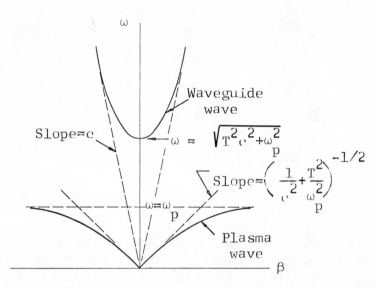

FIG. 1.--Phase characteristics of waves in plasma-
     filled waveguide with infinite axial
     magnetic field.

In addition to increasing the cutoff frequency,
the presence of the plasma allows β^2 to take on
positive real values for $\omega < \omega_p$, thus giving rise
to a propagating wave. Figure 1 shows the phase
velocity versus frequency characteristics[*] of this
additional mode in relation to the perturbed electromagnetic waveguide mode. The lower branch represents the electromechanical or plasmaguide mode
and has a high-frequency cutoff at ω_p with no low
frequency cutoff. Neglecting the free-space wave
number k, the phase velocity of the plasmaguide
wave at low frequencies is approximately

$$v_{ph} = \omega_p a/p_{n\nu} \qquad\qquad (II.31)$$

and can in principle always be made small compared

_____

[*]Such plots are called ω-β diagrams.

with the velocity of light if the guide radius is
made sufficiently small ($\omega_p \ll \omega_{c0}$) and the plasma
frequency is much smaller than the empty guide
cutoff ($\omega_p \ll p_{n\nu}c/a$). This would be a low-phase-
velocity, nondispersive system at low frequencies.
The phase velocity at higher frequencies is always
smaller than the phase velocity at zero frequency,
and is zero at $\omega = \omega_p$.
     One of the interesting features of plasma-
guide modes is that the high-frequency cutoff is
independent of the configuration and depends only
on the plasma frequency. This result is in contrast with the electromagnetic waveguide modes,
where the cutoff frequency is very sensitive to
dimensions. Also in contrast with the electromagnetic waveguide modes (where the number of modes
that can propagate continues to increase with frequency) is the fact that at any frequency within
the passband ($0 < \omega < \omega_p$), all the higher-order
($n > 0$, $\nu > 1$) modes will propagate simultaneously
with the lowest-order mode ($n = 0$, $\nu = 1$), if
they are excited.

     POWER FLOW. The slope of the ω-β curve at
any point indicates the group velocity or velocity
at which energy is carried along in the system.
For the plasmaguide mode the group velocity is
nonzero, which implies that there is a real power
flow associated with these modes.
     The average power flow associated with these
plasmaguide waves is given by

$$\overline{P}_z = \frac{1}{2} \text{ Re } \left\{ \int_\Sigma \underline{E}_1 \times \underline{H}_1 d\sigma \right\} \qquad (II.32)$$

where Σ is the guide area. For the lowest circularly symmetric mode (II.32) becomes

$$\bar{P}_z = \frac{1}{2} \, \text{Re} \left[2\pi \int_0^a \frac{\omega\epsilon_0 \beta E_{1z}^2 (0)}{(k^2 - \beta^2)^2} \, J_1^2 (Tr) \, (Tr) \, d(Tr) \right]$$

$$= \pi \frac{\omega\epsilon_0 \beta}{(k^2 - \beta^2)^2} E_{1z}^2 (0) \, \frac{(Ta)^2}{2} \, J_1^2 (Ta)$$

$$= \pi \left(\frac{\omega}{\beta} \right) \left(\frac{1}{\beta^2} \right) \left(\frac{\epsilon_0}{2} \right) E_{1z}^2 (0) \, (p_{01})^2 J_1^2 (p_{01}) \qquad \text{(II.33)}$$

where k^2 has been neglected as compared with β^2
in the last line. The total power flow is the
sum of the power flows over all of the modes that
are excited. The phase velocity ω/β approaches a
constant value at low frequencies and β goes to
zero as ω. For constant power flow, therefore,
the z component of the electric field E_{1z} becomes
small at low frequencies and in the limit is zero.

SIMPLE PHYSICAL EXPLANATION FOR PLASMAGUIDE
MODES. A useful conceptual model in terms of
electrical transmission lines can be given for
the plasmaguide modes as follows. The total
current density (convection plus displacement)
that flows as a result of an applied field is,
for the longitudinal and transverse coordinates,

$$J_{1zT} = j\omega\epsilon_0 \left(1 - \frac{\omega_p^2}{\omega^2} \right) E_{1z} \qquad \text{(II.34)}$$

$$J_{1rT} = j\omega\epsilon_0 E_{1r} \qquad \text{(II.35)}$$

Multiplying the current densities by an area to
get the total current and calculating the admittance gives

$$\frac{I}{V}\bigg|_z = (\text{constant})_1\left(j\omega + \frac{\omega_p^2}{j\omega}\right) \qquad\qquad (\text{II}.36)$$

$$\frac{I}{V}\bigg|_r = (\text{constant})_2(j\omega) \qquad\qquad (\text{II}.37)$$

The admittance of the plasma in the longitudinal direction is seen to be equal to that of a parallel L-C section, and the admittance in the radial direction is the susceptance of free space. Figure 2 shows a transmission line made of such elements. As can be seen, the passbands of the

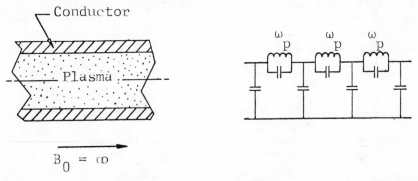

FIG. 2.--Equivalent transmission line for plasma-guide waves.

iterative circuit are the same as predicted by the field analysis, i.e., propagation is possible when the series branch is inductive $(0 < \omega < \omega_p)$ and is not possible when the series branch is capacitive $(\omega > \omega_p)$. Such a transmission-line analog obviously does not predict the ordinary waveguide passbands.

ELECTROMECHANICAL NATURE OF THE PLASMAGUIDE
WAVES. As pointed out earlier, these modes are
electromechanical in nature, i.e., the wave propagation results from the interchange of the
kinetic energy of the electrons with stored energy
in the electric field. A comparison with the electromagnetic modes of propagation, where the wave
propagation results from the interchange of the
electric and magnetic stored energy, is evident
from Fig. 3, which shows the electric and magnetic
fields for the lowest E-mode in a cylindrical
waveguide and the electric field and electron
velocity for the lowest plasmaguide mode in a cylindrical waveguide. Thus it is seen that the
role of the magnetic field for the electromagnetic
waveguide modes has been essentially taken over by
the mass velocity of the electrons.

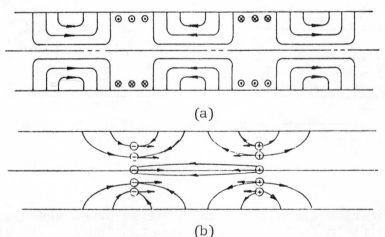

(a)

(b)

FIG. 3.--(a) Electric and magnetic field confi-
          guration for lowest circularly symmetric
          mode in cylindrical waveguide; (b) elec-
          tric field configuration and electron
          velocities for electromechanical plasma-
          guide modes.

REVIEW OF THE FEATURES OF PLASMAGUIDE PROPA-
GATION FOR AN INFINITE AXIAL MAGNETIC FIELD. The
principal feature of plasmaguide propagation is
that a plasma column can, in the absence of any
drift motion, support a mode of wave propagation
below the plasma frequency. The passband for this
mode extends from zero frequency to the plasma frequency and does not depend on the configuration,
except to the extent that the cross section of the
plasma column must be finite. The phase velocity
of the waves, however, depends both on the plasma
frequency and the configuration and very slow waves
are possible for small waveguides. The presence of
the metallic conductor around the plasma is not
essential to the propagation of waves: a plasma
column in free space would have the same qualitative but not quantitative propagation characteristics as the plasma-filled waveguide. All modes
have the same passband and, if excited, propagate
simultaneously. At very low frequencies all of
the modes are nondispersive if the guide-to-plasma
radius ratio is finite. The phase velocities for
typical plasmaguide waves range from a few tenths
to a few hundredths of the velocity of light.
Plasmaguide modes are electromechanical in nature
in that the role played by the magnetic field in
electromagnetic propagation has been taken over by
the mass velocity of the plasma electrons.

3

plasmaguide modes for finite dc magnetic fields

IN CHAPTER II, space-charge-wave propagation in
a plasma-filled waveguide was examined for the
case of an infinite axial magnetic field, with the
help of the complete Maxwell equations. It is of
interest to examine this problem also for finite
magnetic fields and plasma columns only partially
filling the waveguide. The propagation equations
that result from the use of the Maxwell equations
are quite complicated,[11-13] thus making a systematic study of the properties of the space-charge-
wave solutions difficult. A result of the analysis
given in the previous chapter was that the wave
solutions had phase velocities much smaller than
the velocity of light:

$$v_{phase} = \omega/\beta \ll c \qquad (III.1)$$

That means that a free-space wavelength is much
longer than the wavelength of the disturbances in
the waveguide system containing the plasma, and
the instantaneous electric fields are to a good
approximation given by a solution of Laplace's
equation, or in the cases considered here,
Poisson's equation, providing the solutions satisfy the same boundary conditions.[23]

DIELECTRIC CONSTANT OF A PLASMA IN A DC
MAGNETIC FIELD. It is permissible to treat an
ideal electron plasma as described in Chap. II as
an equivalent charge-free, frequency-dependent
dielectric. The dielectric constant for the plasma
in a uniform magnetic field is a tensor because
the components of the electric field and the displacement are no longer related by a simple

isotropic constant.

The components of this tensor are calculated by adding the convection current density* to the free-space displacement current density and equating the sum to the displacement current of the equivalent charge-free region. Thus

$$j\omega\epsilon_0\underline{E}_1 + \rho_0\underline{v}_1 = j\omega\underline{\underline{\epsilon}} \cdot \underline{E}_1 \qquad (III.2)$$

where $\underline{\underline{\epsilon}}$ is the tensor dielectric constant. From the equation of motion (II.7), the components of velocity are

$$j\omega v_{1r} = -\frac{e}{m} E_{1r} - \omega_c v_{1\theta} \qquad (III.3)$$

$$j\omega v_{1\theta} = -\frac{e}{m} E_{1\theta} + \omega_c v_{1r} \qquad (III.4)$$

$$j\omega v_{1z} = -\frac{e}{m} E_{1z} \qquad (III.5)$$

where $\omega_c = eB_0/m$ is the cyclotron frequency. Solving for the components of velocity yields

$$v_{1r} = -\frac{e}{m} \frac{-j\omega E_{1r} + \omega_c E_{1\theta}}{\omega^2 - \omega_c^2} \qquad (III.6)$$

$$v_{1\theta} = -\frac{e}{m} \frac{-j\omega E_{1\theta} - \omega_c E_{1r}}{\omega^2 - \omega_c^2} \qquad (III.7)$$

$$v_{1z} = -\frac{e}{m} \frac{E_{1z}}{j\omega} \qquad (III.8)$$

---

*We neglect the term $\rho_1 v_1$, which is assumed to be small, since it is the product of perturbation quantities.

Using these components of velocity in (III.2) and
solving for the tensor, we obtain

$$\underline{\underline{\epsilon}} = \epsilon_0 \begin{Vmatrix} \epsilon_{rr} & j\epsilon_{r\theta} & 0 \\ -j\epsilon_{\theta r} & \epsilon_{\theta\theta} & 0 \\ 0 & 0 & \epsilon_{zz} \end{Vmatrix} \qquad \text{(III.9)}$$

where

$$\epsilon_{rr} = \epsilon_{\theta\theta} = 1 + \frac{\omega_p^2}{\omega_c^2 - \omega^2} \qquad \text{(III.10)}$$

$$\epsilon_{r\theta} = \epsilon_{\theta r} = \frac{\omega_c}{\omega} \frac{\omega_p^2}{\omega_c^2 - \omega^2} \qquad \text{(III.11)}$$

$$\epsilon_{zz} = 1 - \frac{\omega_p^2}{\omega^2} \qquad \text{(III.12)}$$

and $\omega_p^2 = -\rho_0 e/\epsilon_0 m$ is the electron plasma frequency.

PLASMA COLUMN IN A WAVEGUIDE. Consider a perfectly conducting cylindrical waveguide of radius
b containing a plasma column of radius a submerged
in a finite axial magnetic field B_0. To study the
propagation of waves in this system, the ac magnetic field is set equal to zero,

$$\nabla \times \underline{E}_1 = -j\omega\underline{B}_1 = 0 \qquad \text{(III.13)}$$

in accordance with Eq. (III.1), permitting the ac
electric field to be derived from a scalar

potential

$$\underline{E}_1 = -\nabla \emptyset_1 \qquad\qquad \text{(III.14)}$$

Presumably the approximation is good for slow waves $(v^2_{phase} \ll c^2)$; however, the solutions obtained should be examined to determine whether the magnetic fields are indeed negligible in determining the propagation characteristics. For the equivalent dielectric there is no free charge and

$$\nabla \cdot \underline{D}_1 = \nabla \cdot (\underline{\underline{\epsilon}} \cdot \underline{E}_1) = 0 \qquad\qquad \text{(III.15)}$$

which leads to the differential equation that the potential must satisfy,

$$\nabla \cdot \underline{\underline{\epsilon}} \cdot \nabla \emptyset_1 = 0 \qquad\qquad \text{(III.16)}$$

i.e., Laplace's equation for an anisotropic medium. Written explicitly in cylindrical coordinates Eq. (III.16) becomes

$$\frac{1}{r}\frac{\partial}{\partial r}\left(r\epsilon_{rr}\frac{\partial\emptyset_1}{\partial r} + j\epsilon_{r\theta}\frac{1}{r}\frac{\partial\emptyset_1}{\partial\theta}\right) + \frac{1}{r}\frac{\partial}{\partial\theta}\left(-j\epsilon_{\theta r}\frac{\partial\emptyset_1}{\partial r}\right.$$

$$\left. + \epsilon_{\theta\theta}\frac{1}{r}\frac{\partial\emptyset_1}{\partial\theta}\right) + \frac{\partial}{\partial z}\left(\epsilon_{zz}\frac{\partial\emptyset_1}{\partial z}\right) = 0$$

$$\text{(III.17)}$$

where the fact that $\epsilon_{rz} = \epsilon_{zr} = \epsilon_{\theta z} = \epsilon_{z\theta} = 0$ has been used. Also, using the fact that $\epsilon_{\theta\theta} = \epsilon_{rr}$ and $\epsilon_{\theta r} = \epsilon_{r\theta}$ leads to the following partial differential equation for the potential:

$$\frac{1}{r}\frac{\partial}{\partial r}\left(r\frac{\partial\emptyset_1}{\partial r}\right) + \frac{1}{r^2}\frac{\partial^2\emptyset_1}{\partial r^2} + \frac{\epsilon_{zz}}{\epsilon_{rr}}\frac{\partial^2\emptyset_1}{\partial z^2} = 0 \quad \text{(III.18)}$$

To solve this partial differential equation, assume wave solutions of the form

$$\emptyset_1 = R(r)e^{-jn\theta}e^{-j\beta z} \tag{III.19}$$

and solve the resulting linear differential equation in the radial variable,

$$\frac{1}{r}\frac{d}{dr}\left(r\frac{dR}{dr}\right) - \frac{n^2}{r^2}R - \beta^2\frac{\epsilon_{zz}}{\epsilon_{rr}}R = 0 \tag{III.20}$$

Making the identification

$$T^2 = -\beta^2\frac{\epsilon_{zz}}{\epsilon_{rr}} = -\beta^2\frac{1 - (\omega_p^2/\omega^2)}{1 + [\omega_p^2/(\omega_c^2 - \omega^2)]} \tag{III.21}$$

permits the solutions of (III.20)--Bessel's equation--to be written,

$$R(r) = AJ_n(Tr) + BN_n(Tr) \tag{III.22}$$

where, in this case, $B = 0$, since the fields on the axis must be finite. The complete time-dependent potential and field components are:

$$\emptyset_1(r,\theta,z,t) = AJ_n(Tr) \tag{III.23}$$

$$E_{1r}(r,\theta,z,t) = -AJ_n'(Tr) \tag{III.24}$$

$$E_{1\theta}(r,\theta,z,t) = A\frac{jn}{r}J_n(Tr) \tag{III.25}$$

$$E_{1z}(r,\theta,z,t) = Aj\beta J_n(Tr) \tag{III.26}$$

$$\left. \right\} e^{j(\omega t - n\theta - \beta z)}$$

$$(r < a)$$

Outside the plasma ($a < r < b$) the dielectric constant is ϵ_0 and the differential equation for the potential is given by (III.20) with $\epsilon_{zz} = \epsilon_{rr} = \epsilon_0$. The solutions of this equation are the modified Bessel functions of the first and second kind, and a suitable combination of these functions that satisfies the boundary condition at $r = b$ (i.e., the potential must vanish since $E_{1\theta}$ and E_{1z} are proportional to $\emptyset_1$) is

$$R(r) = C[I_n(\beta r)K_n(\beta b) - I_n(\beta b)K_n(\beta r)], \quad a < r < b$$

(III.27)

Taking $\quad A = [J_n(Ta)]^{-1}$

(III.28)

and $\quad C = [I_n(\beta a)K_n(\beta b) - I_n(\beta b)K_n(\beta a)]^{-1}$

(III.29)

satisfies one boundary condition, i.e., the potential or tangential components of the electric fields must be continuous at $r = a$, the edge of the plasma. The remaining boundary condition at $r = a$ can be satisfied in either one of two ways, which are equivalent. One of these methods is to calculate the charge perturbation at the surface of the plasma column caused by the radial motion of the electrons and to make the normal component of the electric field discontinuous by the amount of the surface charge density associated with the perturbation. Since such a calculation determines the amount of radial polarization (which is already accounted for in the tensor dielectric description of the plasma), it is equally correct to require that the normal component of the displacement must be continuous; the dielectric constant in the plasma is that given by (III.9). The latter of these two methods is easier in application and will be used throughout the present treatment. Requiring the normal displacement to be continuous leads to

$$\epsilon_{rr}(Ta) \frac{J_n'(Ta)}{J_n(Ta)} + n\epsilon_{r\theta}$$

$$= K_e(\beta a) \frac{I_n'(\beta a)K_n(\beta b) - I_n(\beta b)K_n'(\beta a)}{I_n(\beta a)K_n(\beta b) - I_n(\beta b)K_n(\beta a)}$$

$$(III.30)$$

where K_e is the relative dielectric constant of the region outside the plasma. Before we examine Eq. (III.30) for the various solutions of interest, it will be useful to consider the solutions that result for the special case b = a and to see how the plasma-filled waveguide solutions treated in Chap. II are modified when the electrons are allowed to move transversely.

PROPERTIES OF A PLASMA-FILLED WAVEGUIDE. When the plasma completely fills the conducting waveguide, the potential solution is

$$R = AJ_n(Tr) \qquad (III.31)$$

where T is given by (III.21). Requiring the potential to vanish at r = a leads to

$$J_n(Ta) = 0 , \qquad (Ta) = p_{n\nu} \qquad (III.32)$$

Since Ta is merely a numerical constant that depends on the particular mode of interest, the propagation constant can be expressed in terms of

$$\frac{\beta}{T} = \left(\frac{(\omega_p^2/\omega^2) - 1}{1 + [\omega_p^2/(\omega_c^2 - \omega^2)]} \right)^{1/2} \qquad (III.33)$$

Values of this propagation equation are
sketched in Fig. 4. Examination of this figure
reveals that, in addition to modifying the infinite
magnetic-field plasmaguide waves, a noninfinite
magnetic field introduces a backward wave, i.e.,
a wave whose phase and group velocities are oppositely directed. When the magnetic field is large
$(\omega_c > \omega_p)$, the cutoff frequency of the forward wave
remains at ω_p; however, when the magnetic field is
small $(\omega_c < \omega_p)$, the forward-wave cutoff is now at
the cyclotron frequency. The backward-wave branches
have the same high-frequency cutoff at $(\omega_p^2 + \omega_c^2)^{1/2}$,
but have different lower-frequency limits: for
$\omega_p < \omega_c$ the backward-wave branch cuts in at ω_c, and
for $\omega_p > \omega_c$ it cuts in at ω_p. The normalized phase
characteristics for several values of ω_c/ω_p are
given in Fig. 5. It is of particular interest to
note that this backward wave is "structureless"
and is not a spatial harmonic of a periodic
structure.[24]

Perhaps the simplest physical explanation for
the existence of a backward wave can be made with
the aid of the equivalent electrical transmission-
line analog described in Chap. II. The longitudinal and radial admittances within the plasma for
the finite-magnetic-field case are obtained from
the tensor dielectric constant (III.9),

$$\left. \frac{I}{V} \right|_r = (\text{constant})_1 \left[j\omega + \frac{\omega_p^2}{(\omega_c^2/j\omega) + j\omega} \right]$$

$$\left. \frac{I}{V} \right|_z = (\text{constant})_2 \left[j\omega + \frac{\omega_p^2}{j\omega} \right]$$

The transmission-line analog, including the capa-
city from the edge of the plasma column to the
conducting waveguide, is shown in Fig. 6. The

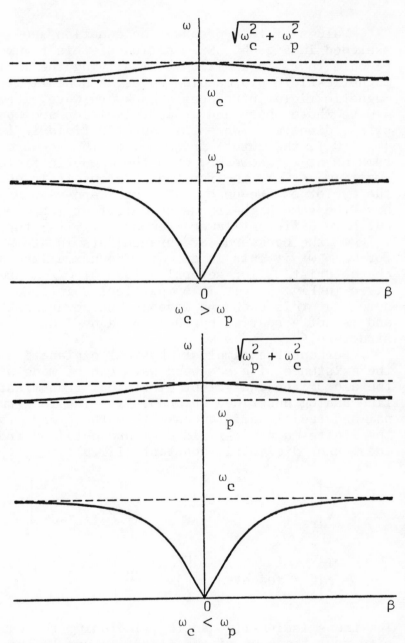

FIG. 4.--Phase characteristics of waves in plasma-
filled waveguide.

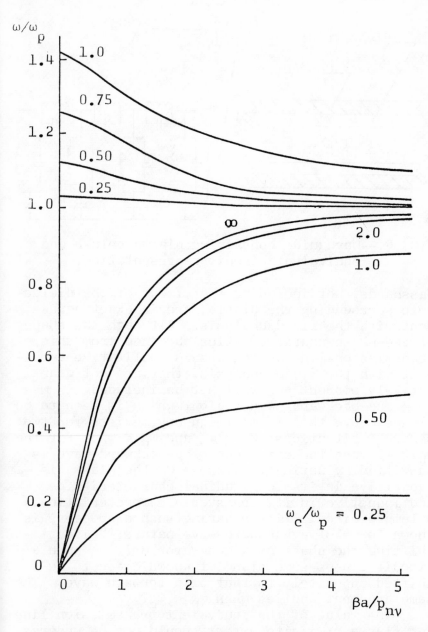

FIG. 5.--Phase characteristics of plasma-filled
        waveguide. $p_{n\nu}$ is νth zero of nth order
        Bessel function of the first kind.

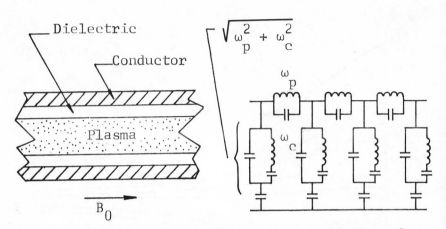

FIG. 6.--Waveguide containing plasma column and
equivalent-circuit representation.

passbands, not including the effect of the dielectric surrounding the plasma, are in exact agreement with the field analysis. Although the shapes
of the phase characteristics obtained from this
transmission-line analog are in qualitative agreement with the field analysis, they are not quanti-
tatively correct and will not be included.

The backward-wave region, which is seen to be
always above the plasma frequency, exists for two
separate situations; $\omega_p > \omega_c$ and $\omega_p < \omega_c$. For the
$\omega_p > \omega_c$ case the existence of a backward wave is
justified by noting that above ω_p the plasma is
capacitive in its longitudinal characteristics
and inductive in its transverse characteristics.
A lumped-circuit filter having such a property is
known to be of a backward-wave nature,[14] i.e.,
shifting the phase of a generator driving such a
circuit causes some plane of known phase to be
shifted oppositely to that of a forward wave. The
same argument applies when $\omega_p < \omega_c$.

The value of the equivalent transmission line
for plasma of finite extent should not be underes-
timated. Such an analog provides a convenient conceptual tool toward understanding the propagation
of waves in plasmas as well as predicting other

modes of propagation. One mode of propagation
that was predicted from transmission-line considerations is the backward wave which results when
the dc magnetic field is made perpendicular to
the guide axis. This mode will be treated in detail in a later section of this chapter; however,
to illustrate the usefulness of the transmission-
line concept, the arguments for its existence will
be given now.

For the case of plasma-filled waveguide in
an infinite axial magnetic field, the transmission
line reduces to series inductors and shunt capacitors below the plasma frequency. Imagine now
that the waveguide is of rectangular cross section
and that the magnetic field is perpendicular to
the guide axis. Since direction of the magnetic
field defines the orientation of the inductive
element, it can be easily seen that the rotation
of the magnetic field has resulted in the interchange of the elements of the transmission line
of the axial magnetic field case. The circuit is
now one of longitudinal capacitors and transverse
inductors and is a backward-wave type.

Returning to the plasma-filled guide in a
finite magnetic field, we note that the properties
of the lower branch are essentially the same as
for the infinite-magnetic-field case, with the
notable exceptions of the cutoff frequency (which
is at ω_c for $\omega_c < \omega_p$) and the low-frequency phase
velocity, which now depends on the magnetic field:

$$v_{ph} = \frac{\omega}{\beta} = \frac{a}{p_{n\nu}} \frac{\omega_p \omega_c}{(\omega_p^2 + \omega_c^2)^{1/2}}$$

where $\omega^2 \ll \omega_p^2$ and $\omega^2 \ll \omega_c^2$.

It is now of interest to compare the magnitudes of the field quantities as obtained by the
rigorous treatment of Chap. I and by the approximate method of this chapter. This comparison is
made below:

Maxwell's Equation:

$$E_{1r} = E_{1z}(0) \frac{-j\beta}{k^2 - \beta^2} TJ_n'(Tr) \qquad (III.34)$$

$$E_{1\theta} = E_{1z}(0) \frac{-\beta}{k^2 - \beta^2} \frac{n}{r} J_n(Tr) \qquad (III.35)$$

$$E_{1z} = E_{1z}(0) J_n(Tr) \qquad (III.36)$$

Quasistatic Approximation:

$$E_{1r} = E_{1z}(0) \frac{j}{\beta} TJ_n'(Tr) \qquad (III.37)$$

$$E_{1\theta} = E_{1z}(0) \frac{n}{\beta r} J_n(Tr) \qquad (III.38)$$

$$E_{1z} = E_{1z}(0) J_n(Tr) \qquad (III.39)$$

Note that neglecting k^2 as compared with β^2 in the Maxwell equation solution gives the same electric field components as the quasistatic approximation. Neglecting k^2 is consistent with the meaning of the quasistatic approximation, which assumes the velocity of light to be infinite.

AC MAGNETIC FIELDS FROM QUASISTATIC APPROXI-MATION. The power-flow calculation made in Chap. II involved the ac magnetic field, which was shown early in this chapter to be sufficiently small to be negligible in determining the propagation char-acteristics of the plasmaguide waves. To obtain an estimate of the power flow for the case at hand, it will be necessary to calculate the ac magnetic-field components approximately. A first-order estimate of these field components is ob-tained by the use of one of the Maxwell equations

$$\nabla \times \underline{H}_1 = j\omega\underline{\underline{\epsilon}} \cdot \underline{E}_1 \qquad (III.40)$$

which in component form is

$$\frac{1}{r}\frac{\partial H_{1z}}{\partial \theta} - \frac{\partial H_{1\theta}}{\partial z} = j\omega\epsilon_0(\epsilon_{rr}E_{1r} + j\epsilon_{r\theta}E_{1\theta}) \qquad (III.41)$$

$$\frac{\partial H_{1r}}{\partial z} - \frac{\partial H_{1z}}{\partial r} = j\omega\epsilon_0(-j\epsilon_{\theta r}E_{1r} + \epsilon_{\theta\theta}E_{1\theta}) \qquad (III.42)$$

$$\frac{1}{r}\frac{\partial}{\partial r}(rH_{1\theta}) - \frac{1}{r}\frac{\partial H_{1r}}{\partial \theta} = j\omega\epsilon_0\epsilon_{zz}E_{1z} \qquad (III.43)$$

where H_{1z} will be set to zero since it is the solution of a second independent differential equation. In a rigorous treatment the H_{1z} would be required to match the boundary condition; however, for the quasistatic approximation the tangential electric field at the boundary that is derived from H_{1z} is negligible. The comparison for the ac magnetic-field components is given below for the plasma-filled waveguide.
From Maxwell's equation

$$B_{1\theta} = -j\frac{\omega}{(k^2 - \beta^2)}\frac{1}{c^2}E_{1z}(0)\,TJ_n'(Tr) \qquad (III.44)$$

$$B_{1r} = \frac{\omega}{(k^2 - \beta^2)}\frac{1}{c^2}\frac{n}{r}E_{1z}(0)\,J_n(Tr) \qquad (III.45)$$

From the quasistatic approximation,

$$B_{1\theta} = -j \frac{\omega}{\beta^2} \frac{1}{c^2} E_{1z}(0) \left[-\epsilon_{rr} TJ_n'(Tr) \right.$$

$$\left. - \epsilon_{r\theta} \frac{n}{r} J_n(Tr) \right] \qquad (III.46)$$

$$B_{1r} = - \frac{\omega}{\beta^2} \frac{1}{c^2} E_{1z}(0) \left[\epsilon_{\theta r} TJ_n'(Tr) \right.$$

$$\left. + \epsilon_{\theta\theta} \frac{n}{r} J_n(Tr) \right] \qquad (III.47)$$

Again in the limit of large magnetic field, and neglecting k^2 as compared with β^2, the rigorous treatment using the Maxwell equations in Chap. II agrees with the results using the quasistatic approximation because $\epsilon_{rr} = \epsilon_0$ and $\epsilon_{r\theta} = 0$.

POWER FLOW FOR PLASMA-FILLED WAVEGUIDE.   To investigate the interaction of moving electron beams with the plasmaguide modes (see Chap. V) it will be necessary to evaluate the average power flow associated with this mode.   The power flow will be calculated here in association with the case discussed, rather than in Chap. V, where the results will be used.
    The power flow for the plasma-filled guide in a finite magnetic field can be calculated using the appropriate field components from (III.37) through (III.39) and (III.47) in (II.33).   For the axially symmetric modes

$$\overline{P}_z = \frac{1}{2} \, \text{Re} \left[2\pi \int_0^a E_{1z}^2(0) \, \frac{\omega}{\beta^3} \, \epsilon_0 \epsilon_{rr} J_1^2(\text{Tr}) \, d(\text{Tr}) \right]$$

$$= E_{1z}^2(0) \, \pi \, \frac{\omega}{\beta} \, \frac{1}{\beta^2} \, \frac{\epsilon_0}{2} \, \epsilon_{rr}(\text{Ta})^2 J_1^2(\text{Ta}) \quad (\text{III.48})$$

Since ϵ_{rr} goes to unity at infinite magnetic field, the power flow given above agrees with the power flow calculated in Chap. II when $k^2 \ll \beta^2$ (see Eq. II.34). Simplifying the above expression by using (III.21) leads to,

$$\frac{2\overline{P}_z}{\pi a^2 \epsilon_0 J_1^2(P_0) E_{1z}^2(0)} = \left(\frac{\omega_p^2}{\omega^2} - 1 \right) \frac{\omega}{\beta} \quad (\text{III.49})$$

which is a sort of normalized power flow. This expression illustrates the fact that the backward-wave passband will always be above the plasma fre-quency since the power flow and phase velocities can have opposite signs only if the exciting fre-quency is above the plasma frequency. The power flow calculated above using the approximate ac magnetic field is in agreement with a calculation of power flow made by multiplying the time-average stored energy per unit length by the group velocity of the waves.[*]

PROPERTIES OF A PLASMA COLUMN IN A WAVEGUIDE. When the plasma does not completely fill the con-ducting waveguide, the properties of propagation are obtained by simultaneously solving (III.21) and (III.30). In contrast to the case of the plasma-filled guide, where one normalized $\omega-\beta$

---

[*]See Chap. V, Power Conservation for Plasma-guide Waves.

diagram describes the properties of <u>all</u> the modes
of higher-order radial and angular variation, the
partially filled guide exhibits diverse properties
for the different modes. A limited study of these
modes has been made with the aid of a digital computer. The results of the study will be presented
for the circularly symmetric mode and the mode of
one angular variation only.

For the lowest circularly symmetric mode, the
forward-wave phase characteristics are as shown in
Fig. 7. The limits of the passbands are obtained
by large and small βa approximations in (III.30).
For the configuration of Fig. 6 the maximum frequency of transmission of the forward-wave passband for $\omega_c < \omega_p$ occurs when

$$\omega = \frac{\omega_p}{\sqrt{2(K_e^2 - 1)}} \left\{ \left[\left(2 - \frac{(K_e^2 - 1)\omega_c^2}{\omega_p^2} \right)^2 \right. \right.$$

$$\left. - 4\frac{\omega_p^2 + \omega_c^2}{\omega_p^2}(K_e^2 - 1) \right]^{1/2} - \left[2 - \frac{(K_e^2 - 1)\omega_c^2}{\omega_p^2} \right]^{1/2} \right\}$$

The cases $\omega_c = 0$ or $K_e = 1$ are particularly sim-
ple, $\omega_{max} = [(\omega_p^2 + \omega_c^2)/2]^{1/2}$; $K_e = 1$, $\omega_c \neq 0$, and
$\omega_{max} = \omega_p/(1 + K_e)^{-1/2}$; $K_e \neq 1$, $\omega_c = 0$. This result was obtained by observing that the maximum
frequency of transmission occurs when $\beta a = \infty$,
and by using the fact that ϵ_{rr} and ϵ_{zz} are both
negative when $\omega_c < \omega < \omega_p$, providing $\omega_c < \omega_p$.
Thus $T^2 > 0$ and approaches infinity as does β^2, so
that (III.30) becomes $\epsilon_{rr}\epsilon_{zz} = K_e^2$. Substituting
the explicit expressions for ϵ_{rr} and ϵ_{zz} and
solving for ω yields the above result. When
$\omega_c > \omega_p$, the passband extends to ω_p. This result
is obtained by noting that $\epsilon_{rr} > 0$, whereas

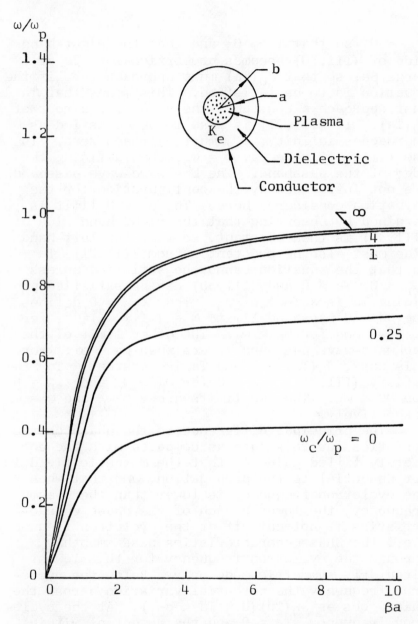

FIG. 7.--Phase characteristics of forward-wave
         passband for lowest-order axially symme-
         tric mode; b/a = 2, K_e = 1.

$\epsilon_{zz} < 0$, so that $T^2 > 0$; and that the right-hand
side of (III.30) becomes proportional to βa at
large βa, so that $J_0(Ta)$ must approach zero if the
equation is to be satisfied. This means that Ta
must approach a constant, the value for a root of
$J_0(Ta)$. If (III.21) is also to be satisfied as βa
approaches infinity, ϵ_{zz} must approach zero. In
the limit of large βa, $\omega = \omega_p$, thus defining the
edge of the passband. The backward-wave passbands
are not influenced by the configuration for the
situation considered here. The $\beta a = 0$ limit is
obtained by observing that the right-hand side of
(III.30) is then constant, so that the left-hand
side must also be constant. From (III.21), Ta = 0,
so that the equation cannot be satisfied unless
$\epsilon_{rr} = 0$, Ta $\neq 0$ and (III.30) can be satisfied providing Ta is a root of J_0. Thus $\epsilon_{rr} = 0$ defines
the $\beta a = 0$ passband limit, $\omega = (\omega_p^2 + \omega_c^2)^{1/2}$, for
$\omega_c > \omega_p$ and for $\omega_c < \omega_p$. The other limit of the
backward-wave passband occurs when $\beta a = \infty$. For
this case, $J_0(Ta) = 0$ and Ta is constant. To
satisfy (III.21), $\epsilon_{zz} = 0$ for $\omega_p > \omega_c$ and $\epsilon_{rr} = 0$
for $\omega_p < \omega_c$. The two limits are $\omega = \omega_p$ and $\omega = \omega_c$,
respectively.

The principal difference in the phase characteristics for this case as compared with the completely filled guide is that the magnetic field is
not essential to the propagation, and that when
the cyclotron frequency is lower than the plasma
frequency, the lower branch of the phase characteristics is not cut off at the cyclotron frequency,
i.e., the phase characteristics pass smoothly
through the cyclotron frequency for this lowest
circularly symmetric mode only. Below the cyclotron frequency the potential variation across the
guide goes as $J_0(Tr)$ ($0 < Ta < p_{01}$). At the cyclotron frequency, Ta = 0 and the potential within
the plasma is uniform. Above the cyclotron frequency (but within the passband) the potential
variation varies as $J_0(jTr) = I_0(Tr)$ ($0 < jTa < \infty$).

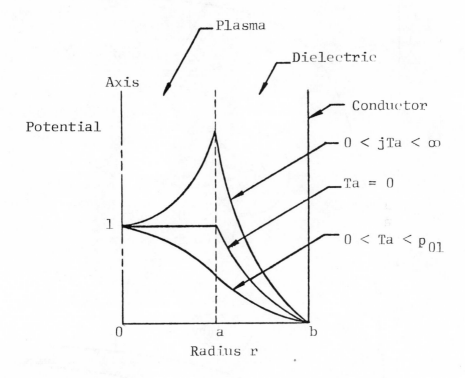

FIG.   8.--Potential variation with radius for
          lowest circularly symmetric mode.

These three cases are illustrated in Fig. 8.   As
the frequency passes through the cyclotron frequency ($\omega_c < \omega_p$) the mechanism of propagation
passes smoothly from one which involves mostly
charge accumulation within the plasma to one which
involves mostly a perturbation or "rippling" of
the surface of the plasma column.   In the limit
of no magnetic field ($\omega_c = 0$), there is no charge
accumulation at all within the plasma.   The properties of these "surface waves" are examined in
detail in the next chapter.
    The phase characteristics of the first few

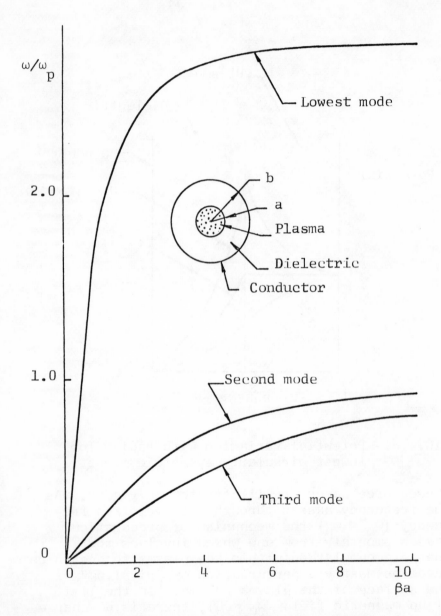

FIG. 9.--Phase characteristics of plasmaguide waves
        showing higher-order radial modes in rela-
        tion to the lowest-order mode; b/a = 2,
        K_e = 1, ω_p/ω_c = 4.

higher-order circularly symmetric modes are shown
in Fig. 9. Notice that only the lowest mode has
the behavior just described, i.e., the phase
characteristics pass smoothly through the cyclo-
tron frequency ($\omega_c < \omega_p$) for the lowest mode only.
All the higher-order radial modes with axial symmetry are cut off at the cyclotron frequency.
This behavior is explained by considering the potential variation (Fig. 10) within the plasma
column. The potential for the mode having one
zero within the plasma varies as J_0 (Tr) (p_{01} < Ta
< p_{02}). As the cyclotron frequency is approached,
Ta approaches p_{01} and the potential outside the
plasma approaches zero, which is to say βa is quite
large. At the cyclotron frequency βa is infinite,
denoting the edge of the passband. Just above ω_c
the propagation equation has no solution for
Ta > 0 and a stop band exists.

FARADAY ROTATION. The principal reason
a mode having one angular variation has been selected is to investigate the possibility of Faraday rotation of the plane of polarization. Such
considerations are important in the analysis of
the perturbation of waveguide modes by the plasma[11]
and seem appropriate for investigation in this
analysis. A superposition of the n ≈ +1 and
n = -1 modes of equal amplitudes yields a composite wave in which the transverse field is polarized in a certain direction. If the n = +1 and
n = -1 modes have different phase velocities, the
direction of polarization of the composite wave
will be rotated as a function of distance along
the guide. For the n = +1 and n = -1 modes to have
different phase velocities, it is necessary for the
propagation equation (III.30) to be an odd function
of n. The propagation equation will be an odd
function of n as long as the plasma does not fill
the waveguide. When the plasma fills the guide,
all higher-order modes of any angular or radial

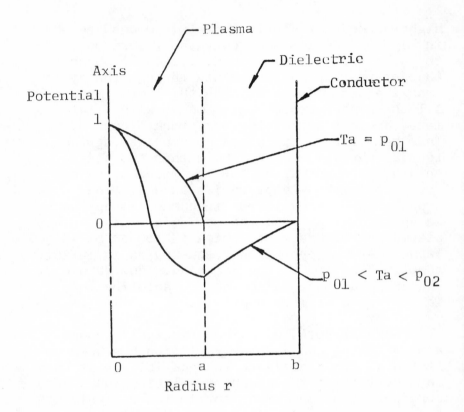

FIG. 10.--Potential variation with radius for cir-
           cularly symmetric mode having one zero
           within the plasma.

order have equal phase velocities for n equal to
plus and minus the same integer and there is
no Faraday rotation. Figure 11 shows the phase
characteristics for the mode of one angular variation for the case of plasma frequency equal to
twice the cyclotron frequency. The lower branches
in Fig. 11 do in fact display different phase velocities for n = ±1. The distance along the guide,
measured in guide wavelengths, for one complete
rotation of the plane of polarization is plotted
in Fig. 12.

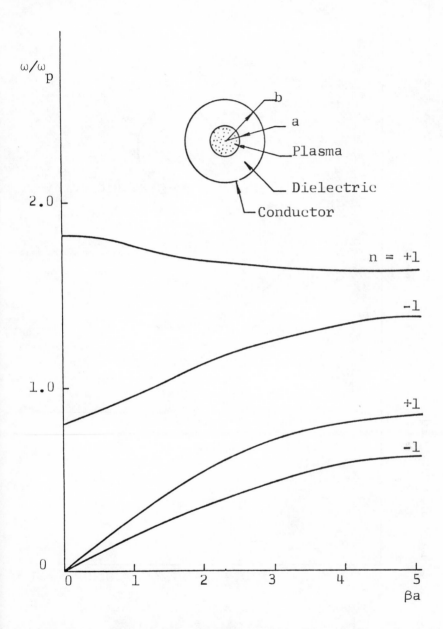

FIG. 11.--Phase characteristics for modes of one
            angular variation in waveguide containing
            plasma column; b/a = 2, K_e = 1, ω_p/ω_c = 2.

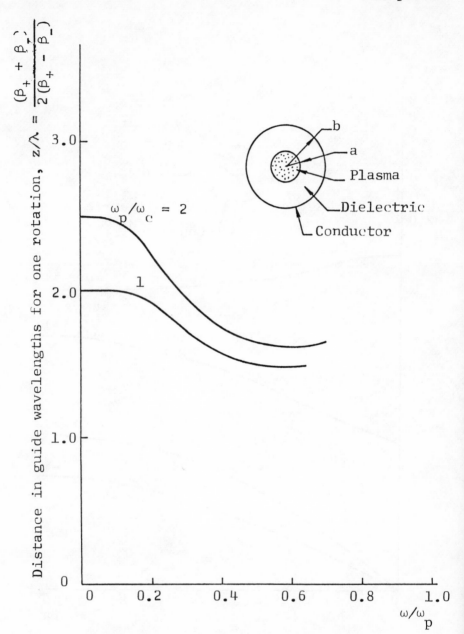

FIG. 12.--Faraday rotation of the plane of polari-
         zation for plasmaguide mode of one angular
         variation; b/a = 2, K_e = 1.

In addition to the lower branches (which were expected), there are other passbands. These other passbands are the surface waves that will be examined in the next chapter. These surface waves are degenerate in angular index in the absence of an axial magnetic field. The addition of the axial magnetic field removes this degeneracy and the modes are split as shown in Fig. 11. For very small magnetic fields these surface waves can also exhibit Faraday rotation; however, no calculation of rotation is given for these upper modes.

PLASMAGUIDE MODE FOR MAGNETIC FIELD TRANSVERSE TO DIRECTION OF PROPAGATION. As a final topic for plasmaguides in finite magnetic fields, consider a waveguide of rectangular cross section completely filled with an ideal plasma, as shown in Fig. 13. The dielectric tensor is

$$\underline{\underline{\epsilon}} = \epsilon_0 \left\| \begin{matrix} \epsilon_{xx} & 0 & 0 \\ 0 & \epsilon_{yy} & j\epsilon_{yz} \\ 0 & -j\epsilon_{zy} & \epsilon_{zz} \end{matrix} \right\| \qquad \text{(III.50)}$$

where

$$\epsilon_{xx} = 1 - (\omega_p^2/\omega^2) \qquad \text{(III.51)}$$

$$\epsilon_{yy} = \epsilon_{zz} = 1 + \frac{\omega_p^2}{\omega_c^2 - \omega^2} \qquad \text{(III.52)}$$

$$\epsilon_{yz} = \epsilon_{zy} = \frac{\omega_c}{\omega} \frac{\omega_p^2}{\omega_c^2 - \omega^2} \qquad \text{(III.53)}$$

Paralleling the analysis for a plasma column in a
waveguide (Eqns. III.13-18), the differential
equation which must be satisfied by the small signal phasor potential is

$$\frac{\epsilon_{xx}}{\epsilon_{yy}} \frac{\partial^2}{\partial x^2} \emptyset_1 + \frac{\partial^2}{\partial y^2} \emptyset_1 + \frac{\partial^2}{\partial x} \emptyset_1 = 0 \qquad \text{(III.54)}$$

Assuming wave solutions of the form

$$\emptyset_1 = X(x) Y(y) e^{-j\beta z} \qquad \text{(III.55)}$$

leads to

$$\frac{\epsilon_{xx}}{\epsilon_{yy}} \frac{1}{X} \frac{d^2 X}{dx^2} + \frac{1}{Y} \frac{d^2 Y}{dy^2} - \beta^2 = 0 \qquad \text{(III.56)}$$

Setting

$$\frac{1}{X} \frac{d^2 X}{dx^2} = -T^2 \qquad \text{(III.57)}$$

gives solutions

$$X(x) = C_1 \sin(Tx) + C_2 \cos(Tx) \qquad \text{(III.58)}$$

The equation in Y is then given by

$$\frac{1}{Y} \frac{d^2 Y}{dy^2} = \frac{\epsilon_{xx}}{\epsilon_{yy}} T^2 + \beta^2 = -S^2 \qquad \text{(III.59)}$$

and the solutions are

$$Y(y) = C_3 \sin(Sy) + C_4 \cos(Sy) \qquad \text{(III.60)}$$

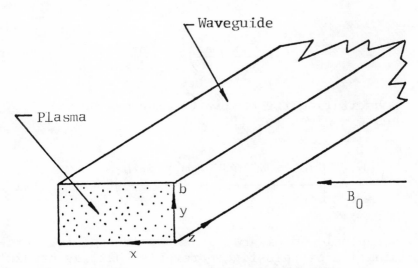

FIG. 13.--Coordinate system used in transverse
         magnetic field analysis.

The boundary condition at the waveguide surface (zero tangential E) is satisfied by taking
$C_2 = C_4 = 0$, $T = m\pi/a$, and $S = n\pi/b$. The potential
and field components are, with $e^{j(\omega t - \beta z)}$ understood,

$$\emptyset(x,y,z,t) = A \sin\left(\frac{m\pi x}{a}\right) \sin\left(\frac{n\pi y}{b}\right) \tag{III.61}$$

$$E_{1x}(x,y,z,t) = -A\left(\frac{m\pi}{a}\right) \cos\left(\frac{m\pi x}{a}\right) \sin\left(\frac{n\pi y}{b}\right) \tag{III.62}$$

$$E_{1y}(x,y,z,t) = -A\left(\frac{n\pi}{b}\right) \sin\left(\frac{m\pi a}{a}\right) \cos\left(\frac{n\pi y}{b}\right) \tag{III.63}$$

$$E_{1z}(x,y,z,t) = jA\beta \sin\left(\frac{m\pi x}{a}\right) \sin\left(\frac{n\pi y}{b}\right) \tag{III.64}$$

The equation of propagation is obtained by
substituting the values of S and T, which satisfy
the boundary condition, in the two terms on the
right of Eq. (III.59) and solving for the propagation constant β:

$$\beta^2 = \frac{\epsilon_{xx}}{\epsilon_{yy}} \left(\frac{m\pi}{a}\right)^2 - \left(\frac{n\pi}{b}\right)^2 \qquad \text{(III.65)}$$

Substituting the explicit expressions for ϵ_{xx} and ϵ_{yy} gives for (III.65)

$$\frac{\beta b}{\pi} = \left[\frac{(\omega_p^2 - \omega^2)(\omega_c^2 - \omega^2)}{\omega^2(\omega_p^2 + \omega_c^2 - \omega^2)} \left(\frac{m\,b}{n\,a}\right)^2 - 1 \right]^{1/2} \qquad \text{(III.66)}$$

A typical ω-β diagram is shown in Fig. 14. Examination of this figure reveals that, as predicted by the transmission-line arguments given earlier in this chapter, there is a backward-wave region from zero frequency up to some frequency that is determined by the particular mode and the configuration. This upper frequency for the backward-wave band is

$$\omega_1 = \frac{1}{2} \left\{ (\omega_p^2 + \omega_c^2) + \left[(\omega_p^2 + \omega_c^2)^2 - \frac{4}{1+\alpha} \omega_p^2 \omega_c^2 \right]^{1/2} \right\}^{1/2}$$

$$0 < \alpha < \infty \qquad \text{(III.67)}$$

where $\alpha = (na/mb)^2$. The fact that α must be finite means that a mode of propagation such as described here does not exist for two parallel planes with plasma between them for a dc magnetic field either parallel or perpendicular to the planes.

Figure 14 also shows a forward-wave region which has a passband from

$$\omega_2 = \frac{1}{2} \left\{ (\omega_p^2 + \omega_c^2) + \left[(\omega_p^2 + \omega_c^2)^2 - \frac{4}{1+\alpha} \omega_p^2 \omega_c^2 \right]^{1/2} \right\}^{1/2}$$

$$0 < \alpha < \infty \qquad \text{(III.68)}$$

$$\omega_1(-), \; \omega_2(+) = \frac{1}{\sqrt{2}} \left\{ (\omega_p^2 + \omega_c^2) \pm \left[(\omega_p^2 + \omega_c^2)^2 \right. \right.$$

$$\left. \left. - \frac{4}{1 + \alpha} \, \omega_p^2 \omega_c^2 \right]^{1/2} \right\}^{1/2}$$

$$\alpha = \left(\frac{nb}{ma} \right)^2 ; \; m,n = 1,2,3, \ldots$$

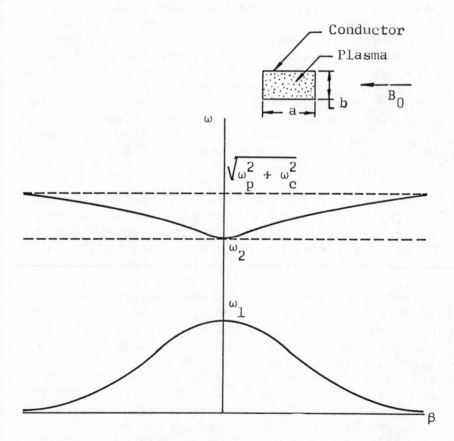

FIG. 14.--Phase characteristics for rectangular
        plasma-filled waveguide with transverse
        dc magnetic field.

up to $\omega = (\omega_p^2 + \omega_c^2)^{1/2}$. This forward-wave mode
would have been predicted by the transmission-line
arguments if a finite magnetic field case had been
considered; it is essentially the backward-wave
region of plasma-filled waveguide in a finite axial
magnetic field with the transmission-line elements
rotated through 90°.

This analysis suggests the existence of still
other interesting propagation phenomena at frequencies near or below the cyclotron or plasma frequency in other configurations. Although such
phenomena are known to exist, the systematic investigation and presentation of the analyses would
be lengthy and not germane to our present purpose,
which is the presentation of the notion that electromechanical modes of a slow-wave nature can propagate and carry energy below the plasma frequency
in finite plasmas in the absence of any drifting
motion to the plasma.

REVIEW OF THE PROPERTIES OF PLASMAGUIDE WAVES
IN FINITE MAGNETIC FIELDS. In contrast to the
finite-magnetic-field case, the plasma-filled waveguide in a finite magnetic field has additional
passbands above either the plasma frequency or the
cyclotron frequency, whichever is largest. The
phase characteristics of these passbands are
those associated with backward waves. These
backward waves are not the conventional spatial
harmonics on a periodic structure. There is no
Faraday rotation for the plasma-filled waveguide,
and the passbands depend only on the cyclotron
and plasma frequencies. The phase velocities of
these waves are usually much smaller than the
velocity of light and depend on the configuration
as well as on the cyclotron and plasma frequencies.
Propagation stops when the magnetic field is reduced to zero.

When the plasma does not completely fill the

waveguide, propagation can exist at zero magnetic
field as well as at higher magnetic fields. For
small magnetic fields the wave propagation involves
both a perturbation of the average charge density
and a rippling of the plasma surface. The phase
velocities of the angular dependent modes are
different for plus and minus the same angular index; and Faraday rotation exists. The surface
waves are now distinct from the body waves and
can also exhibit Faraday rotation.

    Reorienting the magnetic field at right
angles to the waveguide axis also results in propagation. The essential feature is a low-frequency
backward-wave passband. A narrow forward-wave
passband also exists near the plasma frequency or
cyclotron frequency, depending on their relative
magnitudes.

4

plasmaguide waves for zero dc magnetic field

IF THE MAGNETIC FIELD is reduced to zero for the plasma-filled waveguide, propagation is no longer possible; however, if the plasma only partially fills the waveguide, a surface-wave mode of propagation that involves no charge bunching within the plasma is possible. In the absence of a dc magnetic field the plasma is a homogeneous isotropic dielectric and the propagation characteristics of these waves could be investigated by means of the complete Maxwell equations without becoming unduly complicated since mixed modes (i.e., both E and H modes simultaneously present) are not required to match the boundary conditions.[11] However, in anticipation of slow-wave solutions, the quasistatic approximation will again be used, since the results appear in a somewhat simpler form and are correct to a good approximation when $k^2 \ll \beta^2$. Although the plasmaguide modes of propagation involve a mixture of surface rippling of the plasma column and charge accumulation in the interior region of the plasma for small dc magnetic fields ($\omega_c < \omega_p$), enough interesting results are associated with the pure surface wave case ($\omega_c = 0$) to warrant separate discussion.

For zero magnetic field the tensor permittivity for the plasma, Eq. (III.9), reduces to

$$\epsilon = \epsilon_0 [1 - (\omega_p/\omega)^2] \qquad (IV.1)$$

and the equation that must be satisfied by the small signal potential is, from Eq. (III.16),

$$[1 - (\omega_p/\omega)^2] \nabla^2 \phi_1 = 0 \qquad (IV.2)$$

This equation has two solutions:

$$1 - (\omega_p/\omega)^2 = 0 \qquad\qquad \text{(IV.3)}$$

$$\nabla^2 \emptyset_1 = 0 \qquad\qquad \text{(IV.4)}$$

The former solution represents plasma oscillations and, in the case of a stationary plasma, does not imply wave propagation, since any disturbance would (in the absence of collisions or thermal velocities) persist indefinitely at the location of the disturbance. Assuming the exciting frequency to be different from the plasma frequency requires solutions of the latter type, i.e., the potential must satisfy Laplace's equation.

Assuming wave solutions (see Eq. III.19) leads to the modified Bessel's equation (III.20, with $\epsilon_{zz} = \epsilon_{rr} = 1$) and the solutions for the radial function inside and outside the plasma column are

$$R_i = A I_n(\beta r) \qquad\qquad \text{(IV.5)}$$

$$R_o = B[\, I_n(\beta r) K_n(\beta b) - I_n(\beta b) K_n(\beta r)\,] \qquad \text{(IV.6)}$$

where the second solution of the modified Bessel's equation has been omitted inside the plasma since the fields on the axis must be finite. The solution outside has been chosen to satisfy the boundary condition of zero tangential electric field at the conducting boundary of the cylindrical waveguide containing the plasma column. Taking

$$A = [\, I_n(\beta a)\,]^{-1} \qquad\qquad \text{(IV.7)}$$

$$B = [\, I_n(\beta a) K_n(\beta b) - I_n(\beta b) K_n(\beta a)\,]^{-1} \qquad \text{(IV.8)}$$

satisfies the requirement that the tangential electric fields must be continuous at r = a. Applying
the remaining boundary condition, continuity of
normal displacement, leads to the determinantal
equation for the propagation of waves

$$\left(1 - \frac{\omega_p^2}{\omega^2}\right) \frac{1}{K_e} = \frac{I_n(\beta a)}{I_n'(\beta a)} \cdot \frac{I_n'(\beta a)K_n(\beta b) - I_n(\beta b)K_n'(\beta r)}{I_n(\beta a)K_n(\beta b) - I_n(\beta b)K_n(\beta a)}$$

(IV.9)

where K_e is the dielectric constant of the region
between the plasma and the conducting wall of the
waveguide. The solution of this equation is shown
in Fig. 15 for the circularly symmetrical mode.
Propagation is seen to exist from zero frequency
up to the frequency

$$\omega = \frac{\omega_p}{\sqrt{1 + K_e}}$$

(IV.10)

This cutoff frequency is obtained by use of the
large-argument approximations for the modified
Bessel functions and can be physically justified
as follows. The potential variation in the plasma
column and surrounding dielectric is as shown in
Fig. 16(a). For large βa the potential is quite
large at the plasma-dielectric interface and the
fields extend only slightly into the plasma and
dielectric. For this reason, the phase velocity
of the waves at large βa must depend only on the
properties of the interface region. As will be
shown later, this requirement can lead to backward
waves in an isotropic homogeneous plasma filling
a thin dielectric cylinder in free space. Since
$K_e > 1$ for most dielectrics, the circularly symmetric surface waves cannot exist at frequencies
above $\omega_p/\sqrt{2}$. The low-frequency region is

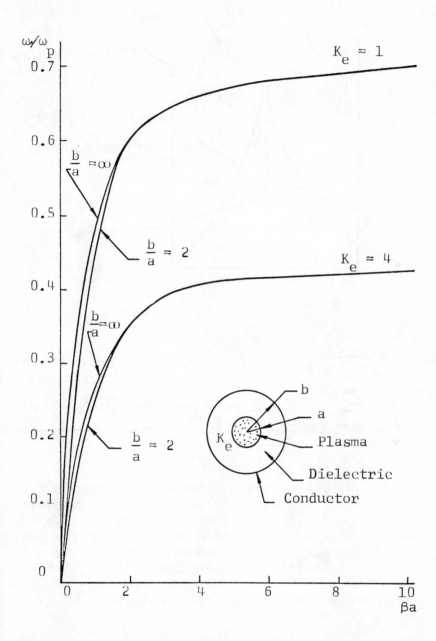

FIG. 15.--Phase characteristics for axially symmetrical surface-wave mode.

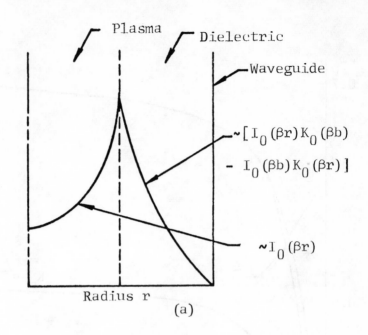

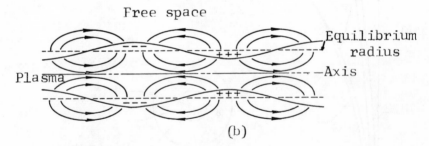

FIG. 16.--(a) Potential variation with radius for
surface waves on plasma column in dielectric-lined cylindrical waveguide; (b)
field distribution and charge perturbation
for circularly symmetric surface wave on
isotropic plasma column.

nondispersive for all finite b/a values:

$$v_{ph}\Big|_{\omega=0} = \frac{\omega}{\beta}\Big|_{\omega=0} = \left[\frac{\log\ (b/a)}{2K_e}\right]^{1/2} \omega_p a \quad (IV.11)$$

When b/a = ∞ (i.e., for a plasma column in an infinite dielectric) the determinantal equation simplifies to

$$\left(1 - \frac{\omega_p^2}{\omega^2}\right)\frac{1}{K_e} = \frac{I_n(\beta a)K_n'(\beta a)}{I_n'(\beta a)K_n(\beta a)} \qquad \text{(IV.12)}$$

The ω-β diagram for this case is also shown in Fig. 15. As can be seen, the cutoff frequency remains at $\omega_p/\sqrt{1 + K_e}$. The low-frequency behavior is, however, not linear:

$$v_{ph} = \omega/\beta = [0.116 + \log_e(1/\beta a)]^{1/2}\,\omega_p a$$

$$\omega^2 \ll \omega_p^2, \quad \beta a \ll 1 \qquad \text{(IV.13)}$$

and the system is dispersive in this region. That the dielectric space surrounding the plasma is essential to the existence of these waves can be understood by observing that making b/a = 1 leads to the degenerate case ω = 0 for all β. That the dielectric space is essential can also be argued by observing that the waves depend on surface-charge accumulation, and the presence of a tight-fitting conducting cylinder prevents such accumulation. The rippling of the boundary of the plasma column is well described by the term "peristaltic." That is, one of the planes where the column has minimum diameter or is constricted, moves with the phase velocity of the wave. The perturbed shape of the plasma column and the electric field distribution are shown in Fig. 16(b).

SIMPLE METHOD FOR OBTAINING LOW-FREQUENCY PHASE VELOCITIES OF PLASMA WAVES. The expression for the low-frequency phase velocity, Eq. (IV.11),

was obtained by using the small-argument approximations for the modified Bessel functions. In
matching the boundary conditions, the ratio of the
normal displacement to the potential was made continuous across the boundary r = a. Passing to the
limit of small βa for this ratio and using the
functions in the region outside the plasma gives
an expression that is independent of βa. Therefore,
it seems appropriate to go directly to the solution
of the differential equation with β = 0. The potential will be a solution of Laplace's equation,

$$\frac{1}{r} \frac{d}{dr} \left(r \frac{dR}{dr} \right) - \frac{n^2}{r^2} R = 0 \qquad (IV.15)$$

The solutions are

$$R = A + B \log r \qquad \text{for } n = 0 \qquad (IV.16)$$

$$R = Ar^n + Br^{-n} \qquad \text{for } n \neq 0 \qquad (IV.17)$$

The application of the method involves writing the
solutions in each of the regions outside the plasma
and, starting with the most remote boundary (where
the boundary condition is presumed to be known such
as the conducting wall of the waveguide), transferring the solution to the next discontinuity,
and requiring that the normal displacement-potential ratio should be continuous across the
boundary. This process is repeated until the surface of the plasma has been reached. At this
point the normal displacement-potential ratio for
the β = 0 solution outside the plasma is equated
to this ratio for the small argument ($\beta a \rightarrow 0$)
solutions inside the plasma, which gives the desired solution. The reason why the β = 0 solution
is not used for the interior of the plasma is that
the normal displacement-potential ratio does not
approach a constant value for small β, but rather

goes to zero as β^2. Thus it would not be possible
to realize a solution of the propagation equation
(IV.9) by using the $\beta = 0$ solution within the
plasma.

This method is most useful in complicated
configurations or for investigating the higher-
order angular variation modes. To illustrate the
method, however, only the simple two-region configuration considered here for the circularly
symmetric case will be used. Other applications
of the method will appear only as results. The
$\beta = 0$ solution of Laplace's equation for axial
symmetry outside the plasma is

$$R_o = A + B \log r \qquad (IV.18)$$

The solution inside the plasma is still given by
Eq. (IV.5). Equating the normal displacement-
potential ratios

$$\left(1 - \frac{\omega_p^2}{\omega^2}\right)\frac{\partial R_i/\partial r}{R_i} = K_e \frac{\partial R_o/\partial r}{R_o} \qquad (IV.19)$$

and evaluating at $r = a$ gives

$$\left(1 - \frac{\omega_p^2}{\omega^2}\right)\beta \frac{I_a'(\beta a)}{I_a(\beta a)} = K_e \frac{1/a}{\log \frac{a}{b}} \qquad (IV.20)$$

where the small-βa forms of the modified Bessel
functions must now be used for the left-hand side.
This procedure leads to the same result as given
in Eq. (IV.11).

PLASMAGUIDE SURFACE WAVES OF ONE ANGULAR
VARIATION. For the $n = 1$ case, the behavior is
as shown in Fig. 17. The upper cutoff frequency

remains at $\omega_p/\sqrt{1 + K_e}$. However, unlike for the
circularly symmetric mode, the lower cutoff is not
at zero frequency, but occurs at some frequency
between zero and the upper cutoff. The lower-
frequency limit can be calculated from the small-β
solution method just described. The result is

$$\omega_{co} = \left(1 + K_e \frac{b^2 + a^2}{b^2 - a^2}\right)^{-1/2} \omega_p \qquad (IV.21)$$

The small-βa limit is in a region where the quasistatic approximation is not necessarily valid, and
the result should be interpreted with caution.
This mode has oppositely directed phase and group
velocities for small βa and large b/a, and is
therefore a backward wave in this region. Examination of the differential equations reveals that
n, the angular index, appears as a squared term
only. Choosing the n = -1 solution would have
therefore led to the same determinantal equation,
which is to say that the angularly dependent modes
of opposite index are degenerate. (We have seen
in Chap. III that the addition of an axial magnetic
field removes this degeneracy.) For the n = +1
mode, the perturbation of the surface of the plasma
column is such that, at any instant of time the
column would be of a helical or serpentine shape;
the reason is that in any one plane the electrons
move together as a disk which executes a small
circular motion at an angular rate equal to the
exciting frequency. A linearly polarized wave
(equal amplitudes n = +1 and n = -1 superposed)
would perturb the plasma column to make it sinusoidally scalloped when viewed at right angles to
the plane of polarization, and to be undisturbed
when viewed along the polarization axis. The
reason for this pattern is that the electrons in
any one plane again move as a disk, except that
now the disk moves sinusoidally in time along the

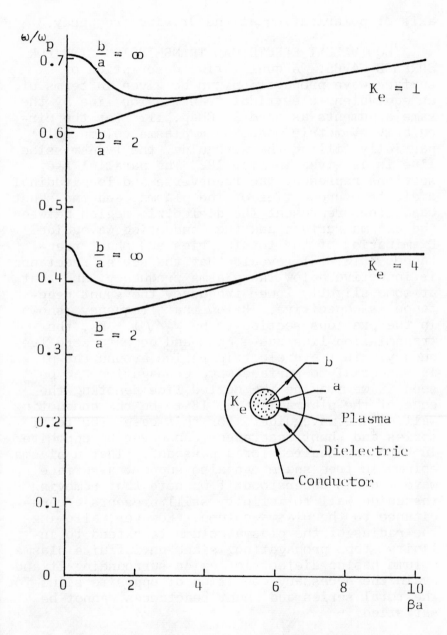

FIG. 17.--Phase characteristics for surface-wave
mode of one angular variation.

axis of polarization at the driving frequency.

EQUIVALENT ELECTRICAL TRANSMISSION LINE FOR
SURFACE WAVES. A qualitative description of
surface-wave propagation can be given in terms of
an equivalent electrical transmission line by the
same arguments as used in Chap. II. For the circularly symmetric modes on a plasma column only
partially filling the waveguide, the transmission
line is as given in Fig. 18. The parallel L-C
sections represent the transverse and longitudinal
dielectric properties of the plasma, and the shunt
capacitors represent the dielectric region between
the plasma surface and the conducting waveguide.
Examination of the total series and shunt reactances (Fig. 18) reveals that the series reactance
is inductive below the plasma frequency, and that
at some slightly lower frequency the shunt reactance is capacitive. Below that frequency (shown
in the previous section to be $\omega_p/\sqrt{1 + K_e}$, the
transmission line has a passband down to zero frequency. That a dielectric region around the plasma
is essential to surface-wave propagation can be
seen if we imagine the dotted line denoting the
edge of the plasma in Fig. 18 to be the conducting
wall of the waveguide. For this case, the total
series and shunt reactances can never be opposite
in sign as required for a passband. That a plasma
column in free space can also support a surface
wave mode is understood if we note that removing
the guide wall to infinity still presents a capacitance to the plasma column. However, allowing
the radius of the plasma column to extend to infinity stops propagation, since an infinite plasma
column has no dielectric region surrounding it and
again the necessary condition of opposite signs for
the total series and shunt reactances cannot be
satisfied.

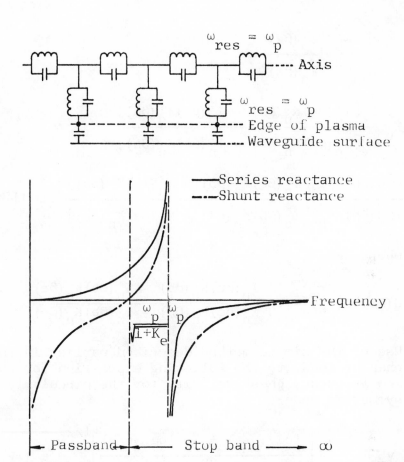

FIG. 18.--Equivalent electrical transmission line
for surface waves on isotropic plasma
column and reactance diagram showing
passband.

BACKWARD SURFACE WAVES ON A PLASMA COLUMN.
Consider now a plasma column of radius a filling
a dielectric cylinder (outer radius b and relative
dielectric constant K_e) in a conducting waveguide
of radius c. The determinantal equation for the
propagation of waves in this system is[*]

---

[*]The method used in obtaining this equation
is outlined in Appendix II.

$$\left(1 - \frac{\omega_p^2}{\omega^2}\right)\frac{I_n'(\beta a)}{I_n(\beta a)} =$$

$$K_e \frac{K_e[I_n'(\beta a)K_n'(\beta b) - I_n'(\beta b)K_n'(\beta a)]}{K_e[I_n(\beta a)K_n'(\beta b) - I_n'(\beta b)K_n(\beta a)]}$$

$$\frac{+[Q(\beta b)/\epsilon_0][I_n(\beta b)K_n'(\beta b) - I_n'(\beta b)K_n(\beta b)]}{+[Q(\beta b)/\epsilon_0][I_n(\beta b)K_n(\beta a) - I_n(\beta a)K_n(\beta b)]} \qquad (IV.22)$$

where

$$Q(\beta b;\beta c,\epsilon_0) = \epsilon_0 \frac{I_n(\beta c)K_n'(\beta b) - I_n'(\beta b)K_n(\beta c)}{I_n(\beta c)K_n(\beta b) - I_n(\beta b)K_n(\beta c)}$$

Use of the simple method described earlier in this chapter leads to the following expression for the low frequency phase velocity for the circularly symmetric mode:

$$v_{ph}\Big|_{\omega=0} = \left[\frac{\log(b/a) + K_e \log(c/b)}{2K_e}\right]^{1/2} \omega_p a \quad (IV.23)$$

The addition of an air space between the dielectric surrounding the plasma and the waveguide is seen to modify the low-frequency phase velocity. This result can be understood from the transmission-line arguments by observing that at low frequencies the inductive reactance of the plasma is linear with frequency (constant inductance) and the phase velocity is determined by the effective inductance of the plasma and by the shunt capacitance from the edge of the plasma to the waveguide. Changing this shunt capacitance by altering the dielectric

configuration should then modify the low-frequency
phase velocity as shown in Eq. (IV.23). Examination
of the large-βa behavior reveals that

$$\omega = \omega_p / \sqrt{1 + K_e} \qquad\qquad (IV.24)$$

when βa goes to infinity. The physical reason is
that, as with the case of the dielectric-lined
plasma-filled waveguide discussed earlier in this
chapter, the potential is a maximum at the plasma-
dielectric interface and fields extend only a
short distance into the two regions when βa is
large. Thus the asymptotic phase velocity should
depend only on the properties of the plasma and the
dielectric immediately surrounding it. For this
case, however, the frequency given by Eq. (IV.24)
is not the maximum frequency of transmission for
the system. An ω-β diagram obtained from Eq. (IV.22)
is shown in Fig. 19. Instead of monotonically
approaching the large-βa limiting frequency, the
ω-β curve rises to a maximum value above this
limit and then approaches the large-βa solution.
This behavior is best explained by considering
two limiting cases. The first is that of a plasma
column in free space, and the second is a plasma
column in an infinite medium of dielectric constant
K_e. The ω-β diagrams for these two cases are shown
in Fig. 20. Imagine now the situation of a plasma
column completely filling a thin dielectric cylinder
that is in turn surrounded by free space. At low
frequencies where βa is small, the effect of the
dielectric cylinder is slight because the waves
extend well into the free-space region and the
ω-β diagram closely follows the upper curve in
Fig. 20. However, when β is sufficiently large
to make $\beta t > 1$ (where t is the thickness of the
dielectric surrounding the plasma), the fields
are confined largely to the dielectric shell and
the phase velocity is determined more by the dielectric and less by the free space surrounding it.

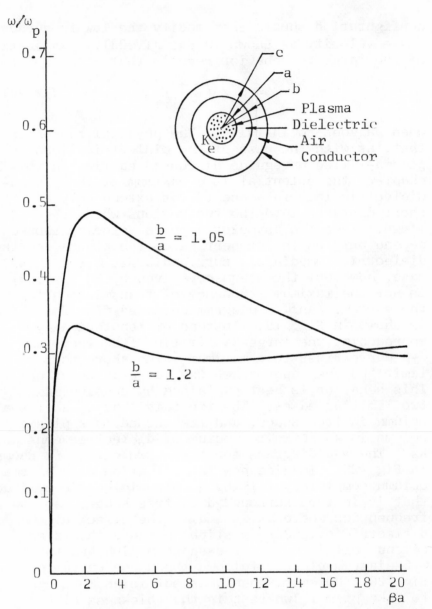

FIG. 19.--Phase characteristics for axially symmetric surface wave on plasma column surrounded by thin dielectric shell; c/b =
2, K_e = 10.

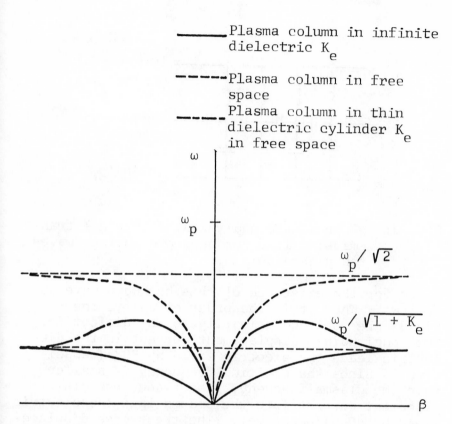

FIG. 20.--Phase characteristics for axially sym-
        metric mode on plasma column illustrat-
        ing reason for backward wave.

In the limit of large βa the solution approaches
the lower curve of Fig. 20. The maximum frequency
of transmission depends primarily on the relative
thickness and on the dielectric constant of the
dielectric surrounding the plasma column. An expression for the maximum frequency of transmission
could be obtained by taking the derivative with
respect to βa in Eq. (IV.22) and equating it to
zero; however, such an expression adds nothing to
the discussion and will therefore not be included.
    A qualitative physical explanation can be

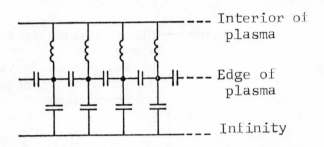

FIG. 21.--Approximate equivalent electrical transmission line for backward surface waves
on plasma column.

given for the existence of this backward wave as
follows. When βt is the order of unity, the
fields are confined primarily to the dielectric.
The longitudinal displacement current in the dielectric leads the electric field by 90° (capacitive). Since the exciting frequency is smaller
than the plasma frequency, the transverse displacement current into the plasma lags the electric
field by 90° (inductive). The transverse displacement current into the free-space region outside
the dielectric leads the electric field by 90°
(capacitive). The equivalent-transmission-line
concept leads to the circuit shown in Fig. 21.
The backward-wave region of such a circuit occurs
when the transverse inductance predominates over
the transverse capacitance. Although the actual
equivalent circuit is much more complex, only the
essential nature of the backward-wave region is
illustrated here; any attempt to include the other
elements would only complicate the issue.

The backward wave described above can be en-
hanced by making the dielectric region thin and
of a material of high relative dielectric constant.
Passing a directed electron beam along the axis
of such a system at a velocity near the phase

velocity of the backward-wave region should result
in interaction and growing waves. If the inter-
action-region length and beam current are correct-
ly chosen, the system should operate as a backward-
wave oscillator.[*]

THE EFFECT OF RADIAL CHARGE-DENSITY VARIATION
ON THE PLASMA-COLUMN SURFACE WAVES. In the course
of performing experiments to verify the various
characteristics of the plasmaguide waves, it became
evident that the variation in charge density with
radius might play a significant role. Figure 22
shows a typical theoretical curve for a uniform
plasma and some typical experimental points. The
experimental points fall below the theoretical
curve for values of βa greater than unity and
appear to be approaching different asymptotes.
Since the large βa behavior is determined by the
properties of the plasma-dielectric interface
region, the observed experimental asymptote could
be attributed to a lower charge density at the
edge of plasma column. To investigate such a
possibility, the differential equation for the
potential inside the plasma column was solved
assuming a parabolic variation in charge density
with radius. The solution obtained was then
matched to the solution outside.

Consider a cylindrical isotropic plasma column
of radius a whose charge density is a function of
radius only. Regarding the plasma as a spatially
dependent dielectric requires the potential to be
a solution of Laplace's equation for an inhomo-
geneous medium,

$$\nabla \cdot \epsilon(r) \nabla \emptyset_1 = 0 \qquad\qquad (IV.25)$$

---

[*]The subject of interaction is treated in
detail in Chap. V.

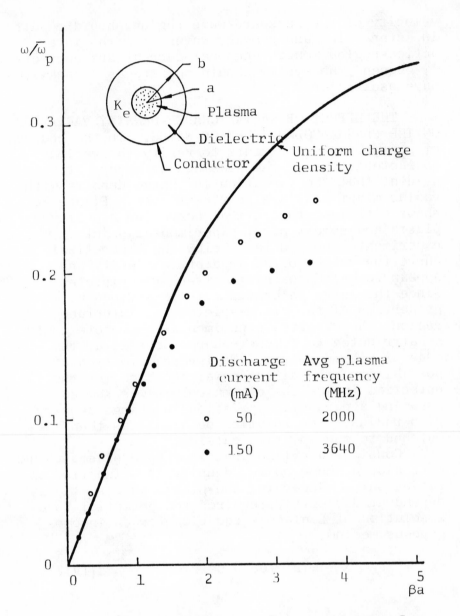

FIG. 22.--Theoretical phase characteristics for
surface waves with experimental points;
b/a = 1.2, K_e = 4.62.

if the quasistatic approximation is assumed. Assuming wave solutions of the form

$$\emptyset_1 = R(r)e^{-jn\theta}e^{-j\beta z} \qquad (IV.26)$$

leads to the following differential equation for
the radial function:

$$\left[\frac{d^2}{dr^2} + \left(\frac{1}{r} + \frac{1}{\epsilon}\frac{d\epsilon}{dr}\right)\frac{d}{dr} - \left(\beta^2 + \frac{n^2}{r^2}\right)\right]R(r) = 0 \qquad (IV.27)$$

Let the radial charge density variation be given
by

$$\rho(r) = \rho_a[1 - \alpha(r/a)^2] \qquad (IV.28)$$

where ρ_a is the axis charge density and α is a
parameter between zero and unity which determines
the degree of radial charge variation. The permittivity for this parabolic charge density
variation is

$$\epsilon(r) = \epsilon_0\left[1 - \frac{\omega_{pa}^2}{\omega^2}\left(1 - \alpha\frac{r^2}{a^2}\right)\right] \qquad (IV.29)$$

where $\omega_{pa}^2 = -\rho_a e/\epsilon_0 m$ is the plasma frequency on
the axis.
    If we define a dimensionless independent var-
iable $\xi = \beta r$ and a dimensionless variable
$f = \omega/\omega_{pa}$, the differential equation in the radial
function becomes

$$\left[\frac{d^2}{d\xi^2} + \left(\frac{1}{\xi} + \frac{2}{\xi^2 - G}\right)\frac{d}{d\xi} - \left(1 - \frac{n^2}{\xi^2}\right)\right]R(\xi) = 0 \qquad (IV.30)$$

where $G = (1 - f^2)(\beta a)^2/\alpha$. To solve this differential equation, multiply through by $\xi^2(\xi^2 - G)$ and assume a power-series solution of the form* (only the n = 0 mode is considered)

$$R(\xi) = \sum_{i=0}^{\infty} C_i \xi^i \qquad (IV.31)$$

The recursion relation obtained for the C_i's is

$$C_{i+4} = \frac{1}{(i + 4)^2} \left[\frac{(i + 2)(i + 4)C_{i+2} - C_i}{G} + C_{i+2} \right]$$
$$(IV.32)$$

Examination of the power series that results from substituting Eq. (IV.31) in the differential equation (IV.30) reveals that the coefficient of the first power term, C_1, must be zero for a solution. Then C_3 must be zero. By the recursion relation, all odd-power terms in the series are then zero; C_0 is arbitrary because it multiplies the indicial equation, which is equal to zero. (The second solution of the differential equation is singular at the origin and is therefore not of interest and will be excluded.) The first few coefficients of the power series and the general term are

$$C_2 = \frac{C_0}{4}$$

$$(IV.33)$$

$$C_4 = \frac{C_0}{64} + \frac{C_0}{16G}$$

---

*This differential equation has the origin as a regular point and the roots of the indicial equation are identical and zero.

$$C_6 = \frac{C_0}{2^6 (3!)^2} + \left[\frac{1}{2^6 G} + \frac{1}{24 G^2} \right] C_0$$

$$C_8 = \frac{C_0}{2^8 (4!)^2} + \left[\frac{2}{2^6 \cdot 3G} + \frac{63}{2^{10} G^2} + \frac{1}{32 G^3} \right] \quad \text{(IV.33)}$$

$$C_{2i} = \left[\frac{1}{2^{2\xi} (i!)^2} + \sum_{v=0}^{i-2} \frac{b_{vi}}{G^{v+1}} \right] C_0$$

Setting $C_0 = 1$ and comparing the power series solution just obtained with power series for the modified Bessel function of the first kind reveals that the solution can be expressed as the Bessel function plus a correction term,

$$R_0(\xi) = I_0(\xi) + \sum_{i=0}^{\infty} \left[\sum_{v=0}^{i} \frac{b_{v,2i}}{G^{v+1}} \right] \xi^{2(i+2)} \quad \text{(IV.34)}$$

where the b_{vi}'s are determined from the recursion relation.

To examine how the radial charge variation affects the propagation of waves, it is necessary to consider a specific configuration. For the case of the plasma column filling a dielectric-lined waveguide of radius b, the solutions are

$$\emptyset_{1i} = A \frac{R_0(\xi)}{R_0(\beta a)} \qquad \left. \begin{array}{l} \\ \\ \end{array} \right\} r < a \quad \text{(IV.35)}$$

$$\left. \begin{array}{l} \\ \end{array} \right\} e^{j(\omega t - \beta z)}$$

$$\emptyset_{1o} = A \frac{I_0(\xi) K_0(\beta b) - K_0(\xi) I_0(\beta b)}{I_0(\beta a) K_0(\beta b) - K_0(\beta a) I_0(\beta b)} \quad \left. \begin{array}{l} \\ \end{array} \right\} a < r < b$$

$$\text{(IV.36)}$$

where subscripts o and i denote the dielectric and

plasma regions, respectively, and the boundary condition on the tangential electric field has already been satisfied. Requiring the normal displacement to be continuous leads to the following propagation equation:

$$
\left[1 - \frac{1}{f^2} (1 - \alpha) \right] \frac{I_1(\beta a) + \sum_{i=0}^{\infty} \left(\sum_{v=0}^{i} \frac{b_{v,2i+4}}{(1-f^2)^{v+1}} \right)}{I_0(\beta a) + \sum_{i=0}^{\infty} \left(\sum_{v=0}^{i} \frac{b_{v,2i+4}}{(1-f^2)^{v+1}} \right)}
$$

$$
\frac{(2i + 4)(\beta a)^{2i+3}}{\dfrac{\alpha^{v+1}}{(\beta a)^{2v+2}} \Big) \beta a^{2i+4}} = K_e \frac{I_1(\beta a) K_0(\beta b) + I_0(\beta b) K_1(\beta a)}{I_0(\beta a) K_0(\beta b) - I_0(\beta b) K_0(\beta a)}
$$

$$\text{(IV.37)}$$

An ω-β curve obtained from Eq. (IV.37) showing the effect of charge density variation with radius is given in Fig. 23. As can be seen, the ω-β curves break away from the ω-β curve for uniform charge density for $\beta a > 1$. The reason is that for $\beta a > 1$, the phase velocity of the waves depends more on the edge charge density than on the average charge density.

It is now of interest to examine the solutions for two limiting cases, $\beta a = 0$ and $\beta a = \infty$. From Eq. (IV.28) and the definition of plasma frequency, we have

$$
\omega_{pe} = \sqrt{1 - \alpha} \; \omega_p a \qquad \text{(IV.38)}
$$

where ω_{pe} is the edge plasma frequency. Since the phase velocity of the waves at large βa depends only on the plasma-dielectric interface properties,

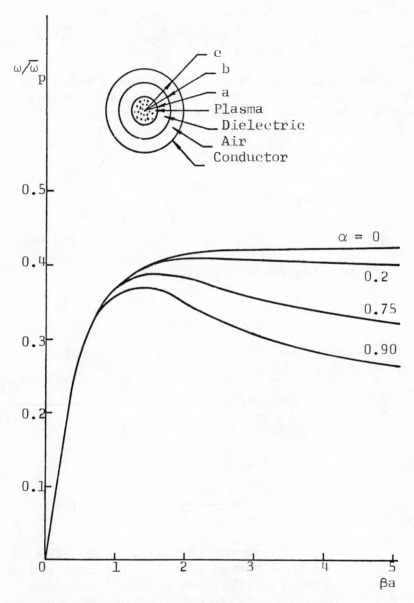

FIG. 23.--Phase characteristics of surface waves
        showing effect of variation of charge
        density with radius; c/b = 2, b/a = 1.2,
        K_e = 4.62.

$$\omega\Big|_{\beta a=\infty} = \frac{\sqrt{1 - \alpha}}{\sqrt{1 + K_e}} \omega_{pa} \qquad \text{(IV.39)}$$

To obtain the low-frequency phase velocity, it is necessary to examine the radial functions inside the plasma for small βa. Keeping first-order terms in βa for the correction term to the modified Bessel function (see Eq. IV.31) gives

$$\lim_{\beta a \to 0} F(\beta a) = \frac{(\beta a)^2}{8} \sum_{i=0}^{\infty} \frac{1}{(i + 2)} \left(\frac{\alpha}{1 - f^2}\right)^{i+1}$$

$$\text{(IV.40)}$$

where F denotes the correction term,

$$R_0(\xi) = I_0(\xi) + F(\xi;G) \qquad \text{(IV.41)}$$

If we define $r = \alpha/(1 - f^2)$, the series in Eq. (IV.40) can be written as

$$S = \sum_{n=0}^{\infty} \frac{r^{n+1}}{n + 2} = \frac{r}{2} + \frac{r^2}{3} + \frac{r^3}{4} + \cdots \qquad \text{(IV.42)}$$

The sum of this series is

$$S = \frac{1}{r} \log \frac{1}{1 - r} - 1 \qquad \text{(IV.43)}$$

This series is convergent for all $r^2 < 1$. The condition for convergence is satisfied at $f = 0$ if $\alpha < 1$. Thus the solutions obtained are good at $f = 0$ for all cases except that of zero charge density at the edge. Since F is of order $(\beta a)^2$ and I_0 is of order $(\beta a)^0$, the radial function

approaches unity in the limit of small βa when
the series is convergent. Keeping the first-order
terms in βa for the derivative of the correction
term gives

$$\lim \frac{dF(\beta r)}{dr}\Bigg|_{r=a} = \beta \frac{\beta a}{4} \sum_{i=0}^{\infty} \left(\frac{\alpha}{1 - f^2}\right)^{i+1}$$

$$= \beta \frac{\beta a}{4} \frac{\dfrac{\alpha}{1 - f^2}}{[1 - \alpha/(1 - f^2)]} \qquad \text{(IV.44)}$$

which, as before, is valid for all $[\alpha/(1 - f^2)]^2$
< 1; and the arguments about range of validity of
the f = 0 solution also apply here.

Using the small-βa approximations for the
modified Bessel functions and the results for the
small βa behavior of the radial functions within
the plasma obtained above gives for the zero frequency phase velocity, we obtain

$$v_{ph}\Big|_{\omega=0} = \left[\frac{\log\,(b/a)}{2K_e}\right]^{1/2} \sqrt{1 - \frac{\alpha}{2}}\ \omega_p a \qquad \text{(IV.45)}$$

Since the average value of the parabolic distribution is

$$\bar{\rho} = \frac{1}{\pi a^2} \int_0^a \int_0^{2\pi} \rho(r)r\ dr\ d\theta = \rho_a\left(1 - \frac{\alpha}{2}\right) \qquad \text{(IV.46)}$$

the expression for the phase velocity becomes

$$v_{ph}\Big|_{\omega=0} = \left[\frac{\log\,(b/a)}{2K_e}\right]^{1/2} \omega_p a \qquad \text{(IV.47)}$$

where $\bar{\omega}_p^2 = -\bar{\rho}e/\epsilon_0 m$ is the average plasma frequency. The low-frequency phase velocity is thus
seen to be constant; i.e., the system is nondispersive and depends only on the average charge
density, whereas the large-βa behavior is determined primarily by the edge plasma frequency.

A potentially useful plasma diagnostic tool
is indicated here in that two measurements should
in principle determine the axis charge density and
the best parabolic fit to the actual charge density.
These two measurements are the low-frequency phase
velocity and the frequency for which $\beta a = \infty$. The
first measurement gives directly the average plasma
frequency for the column as a whole. Unfortunately
an experimental measurement of the frequency for
which βa is infinite is difficult, since at large
βa the group velocity of the waves is high, the
losses are large,* and the large-βa frequency is
not always the maximum frequency of transmission.**
An alternate method of measuring the variation in
radial charge density that avoids the above diffi-
culties is to obtain a family of ω-β diagrams in
the parameter α and then to compare the experimental results with theoretical curves and select
the value of α that gives best agreement.[25]

POWER FLOW ASSOCIATED WITH SURFACE WAVES ON
A PLASMA COLUMN. In Chap. V, where the subject of
interaction of moving electron beams and the plasmaguide modes of propagation is treated, we shall
need expressions for the power flow associated
with the various plasmaguide modes. The expressions
for the power flow in plasma-filled waveguides

---

*Losses are treated in Chap. V.
**The arguments concerning backward waves and
the maximum frequency of transmission for the
three-region problem given in the previous section
apply here.

given in the previous two chapters are not satisfactory since there is no power flow at zero magnetic field for the cases examined (i.e., when
b = a).

Consider a homogeneous isotropic plasma column
of radius a in free space. For the circularly
symmetric mode, the potential and electric field
components are

$$\left.\begin{array}{l} \phi_{1i}(r,z,t) \;\; = A \; \dfrac{I_0(\beta r)}{I_0(\beta a)} \\[3ex] E_{1zi}(r,z,t) = j\beta A \; \dfrac{I_0(\beta r)}{I_0(\beta a)} \\[3ex] E_{1ri}(r,z,t) = \beta A \; \dfrac{I_1(\beta r)}{I_0(\beta a)} \end{array}\right\} e^{j(\omega t - \beta z)} \quad \begin{array}{l} r < a \\[1ex] \text{(IV.48)} \end{array}$$

$$\left.\begin{array}{l} \phi_{1o}(r,z,t) \;\; = A \; \dfrac{K_0(\beta r)}{K_0(\beta a)} \\[3ex] E_{1zo}(r,z,t) = j\beta A \; \dfrac{K_0(\beta r)}{K_0(\beta a)} \\[3ex] E_{1ro}(r,z,t) = +\beta A \; \dfrac{K_1(\beta r)}{K_0(\beta a)} \end{array}\right\} e^{j(\omega t - \beta r)} \quad \begin{array}{l} a < r < \infty \\[1ex] \text{(IV.49)} \end{array}$$

where β is a solution of Eq. (IV.21) with n = 0.
The ac magnetic fields were set equal to zero in
the determination of the propagation characteristics
by the quasistatic approximation. A first-order
estimate of their value that is consistent with
this approximation is obtained with the aid of

one of the Maxwell equations, Eq. (II.2). The
result is

$$H_{1\theta i}(r,z,t) = (\omega/\beta)\epsilon_0[1 - (\omega_p/\omega)^2] E_{1ri}(r,z,t)$$

$$r < a \qquad\qquad\qquad (IV.50)$$

$$H_{1\theta o}(r,z,t) = (\omega/\beta)\epsilon_0 E_{1ro}(r,z,t) \qquad a < r < \infty$$

$$\qquad\qquad\qquad\qquad (IV.51)$$

The time-average power flow is, from Eq. (II.33),

$$\bar{P}_z = A^2 \pi\epsilon_0 \frac{\omega}{\beta}\left\{\left(1 - \frac{\omega_p^2}{\omega^2}\right)\int_0^{\beta a}\left[\frac{I_1(\beta r)}{I_0(\beta a)}\right]^2 (\beta r)\ d(\beta r)\right.$$

$$\left. + \int_{\beta a}^{\infty}\left[\frac{K_1(\beta r)}{K_0(\beta a)}\right]^2 (\beta r)\ d(\beta r)\right\} = A^2 \frac{(\beta a)^2}{2}\pi\epsilon_0\frac{\omega}{\beta}$$

$$\left\{\left(1 - \frac{\omega_p^2}{\omega^2}\right)\left[\frac{I_1^2(\beta a) - I_0(\beta a)I_2(\beta a)}{I_0^2(\beta a)}\right]\right.$$

$$\left. -\left[\frac{K_1^2(\beta a) - K_0(\beta a)K_2(\beta a)}{K_0^2(\beta a)}\right]\right\} \qquad (IV.52)$$

The power flow is seen to be zero at both zero
frequency and at the upper cutoff frequency and
presumably has a maximum value between these limits. The power flow calculated above using the
approximate ac magnetic field is in agreement
with a calculation of power flow made by multiplying

the time average stored energy per unit length by
the group velocity of the waves.*

REVIEW OF THE FEATURES OF PLASMAGUIDE PRO-
PAGATION FOR ZERO DC MAGNETIC FIELD. In the absence of an axial magnetic field or drifting
motion, a homogeneous, isotropic plasma column
only partially filling a waveguide can support a
slow-surface-wave, electromechanical mode of propagation. The fields associated with this mode
are strongest at the surface of the plasma and de-
cay exponentially with radius from the plasma surface. The surface is perturbed when the plasma
column is driven at some frequency within the
passband, and the time-dependent shape of the
plasma column is peristaltic. The surface waves
for two-region configurations have an upper frequency cutoff that depends only on the dielectric
properties just outside the plasma column and the
charge density just within the plasma column. The
circularly symmetric mode is nondispersive at low
frequencies; the phase velocity depends on the
average charge density of the plasma column and on
the capacitance presented to the column by its
surroundings. Backward waves can exist for the
circularly symmetric mode when the plasma column
in free space is surrounded by a thin dielectric
shell. The linearly polarized mode of one angular
variation also exhibits a backward-wave property
and has a nonzero lower frequency limit. It is
also dispersive over the entire passband. The
plane of polarization is not rotated as the wave
travels down the guide because of degeneracy of
the right- and left-hand circularly polarized
components.

Perhaps the most useful feature associated
with the surface-wave propagation is that of

---

*See Chap. V, Power Conservation for Plasma-
guide Waves.

plasma diagnostics. Comparison of theory and experiment provides a means of determining such
properties as the average plasma frequency and
the charge-density distribution.

5

interaction of an electron beam with the plasmaguide modes

THE ELECTROMECHANICAL MODES of propagation in plasma columns discussed in the preceding chapters usually can have phase velocities much smaller than the velocity of light. For instance, the phase velocity of the waves in a plasma-filled waveguide is $v_{ph} = \omega_p a / p_{n\nu}$ and can be made quite small if the waveguide radius or plasma frequency is made small, i.e., if $\omega_p a / p_{n\nu} \ll c$. Since almost any circuit capable of supporting a slow wave can be used to interact with the space-charge waves of a moving electron beam, it seems reasonable to expect that the plasmaguide modes could be used as such a circuit. Of particular interest is the possibility of allowing an electron beam to interact with any of the backward-wave plasmaguide modes described earlier (Chaps. III and IV), making a "structureless" backward-wave oscillator. Such a backward-wave oscillator might be useful in generating very high microwave frequencies. The problem of achieving millimeter waves would be shifted from fabrication of very small and delicate slow-wave circuits to that of obtaining high electron densities or large magnetic fields. Knowledge of the electron-beam characteristics (velocity, etc.) and the resulting frequency of oscillation gives a good measure of the plasma frequency, thus providing a plasma diagnostic tool.

The rate of growth for the interaction of an electron beam with the plasmaguide modes is obtained by two methods. The first is a field analysis which is exact to within the approximation of the quasi-static analysis used in this paper. The second method uses the notion of an interaction impedance[15] and calculates the traveling-wave-tube interaction parameter C for several cases including the backward wave. The difficulty of solving the resultant transcendental equation obtained in the field analysis restricts the solution here to a simple case which will be used to check the validity of the approximate method for the same case.

FIELD ANALYSIS OF ELECTRON-BEAM PLASMAGUIDE INTERACTION. Consider a smooth, perfectly conducting cylindrical waveguide of radius b containing an electron beam of radius a and completely filled with a stationary ideal plasma; let the finite axial magnetic field be B_0. The tensor dielectric constant within the moving beam ($r < a$) is easily obtained from the tensor dielectric constant (Eq. III.9) by adding the susceptance of an additional charge column which has been modified by a coordinate transformation (Chap. VI). With the same notation for the components of the tensor dielectric as in Eq. (III.4), the components for the beam-plasma region are

$$\epsilon_{rr} = \epsilon_{\theta\theta} = 1 + \frac{\omega_p^2}{\omega_c^2 - \omega^2} + \frac{\omega_{pb}^2}{[\omega_c^2 - (\omega - \beta u_0)^2]} \quad (V.1)$$

$$\epsilon_{r\theta} = \epsilon_{\theta r} = \frac{\omega_c}{\omega} \frac{\omega_p^2}{(\omega_c^2 - \omega^2)} + \frac{\omega_c}{(\omega - \beta u_0)} \cdot$$

$$\cdot \frac{\omega_{pb}^2}{[\omega_c^2 - (\omega - \beta u_0)^2]} \quad (V.2)$$

$$\epsilon_{zz} = 1 - \frac{\omega_p^2}{\omega^2} - \frac{\omega_{pb}^2}{(\omega - \beta u_0)^2} \quad (V.3)$$

where

$$\omega_p^2 = - \rho_0 e / \epsilon_0 m \quad \text{"plasma" plasma frequency}$$

$$\omega_{pb}^2 = - \rho_{0b} \, e / \epsilon_0 m \quad \text{beam plasma frequency}$$

$$\omega_c = (e/m) B_0 \ \text{cyclotron frequency}$$

$$u_0 = \sqrt{2eV_0/m} \ \text{dc beam velocity}$$

The dielectric constant without the beam is obtained by setting ω_{pb} equal to zero, which gives Eq. (III.9).

To study the propagation and possible growth of waves in this system, the quasistatic approximation will again be used. The differential equation that must be satisfied by the radial function is obtained directly from Eq. (III.20):

$$\frac{1}{r} \frac{d}{dr} \left(r \frac{dR}{dr} \right) - \frac{n^2}{r^2} R + T_{1,2}^2 R = 0 \qquad (V.4)$$

where inside the beam

$$T_1^2 = -\beta^2 \frac{\epsilon_{zz1}}{\epsilon_{rr1}} = -\beta^2 \frac{1 - \dfrac{\omega_p^2}{\omega^2} - \dfrac{\omega_{pb}^2}{(\omega - \beta u_0)^2}}{1 + \dfrac{\omega_p^2}{\omega_c^2 - \omega^2} + \dfrac{\omega_{pb}^2}{(\omega - \beta u_0)^2}} \qquad (V.5)$$

and outside the beam

$$T_2^2 = -\beta^2 \frac{\epsilon_{zz2}}{\epsilon_{rr2}} = -\beta^2 \frac{1 - \dfrac{\omega_p^2}{\omega^2}}{1 + \dfrac{\omega_p^2}{\omega_c^2 - \omega^2}} \qquad (V.6)$$

Suitable solutions in the two regions are

$$R_1(r) = AJ_n(T_1 r) \quad \text{inside the beam} \quad (a < r) \quad (V.7)$$

$$R_2(r) = G[J_n(T_2 r)N_n(T_2 b) - J_n(T_2 b)N_n(T_2 r)]$$

$$\text{outside the beam} \quad (a < r < b) \quad (V.8)$$

Matching the ratio of normal displacement to tangential electric field at the beam-plasma interface ($r = a$) leads to the following determinantal equation:

$$\epsilon_{rr1}(T_1 a) \frac{J_n'(T_1 a)}{J_n(T_1 a)} + n\epsilon_{r\theta_1} = \epsilon_{rr2}(T_2 a) \cdot$$

$$\frac{J_n'(T_2 a)N_n(T_2 b) - J_n(T_2 b)N_n'(T_2 a)}{J_n(T_2 a)N_n(T_2 b) - J_n(T_2 b)N_n(T_2 a)} + n\epsilon_{r\theta_2} \qquad (V.9)$$

Equation (V.9) and the equations defining the radial separation constants, Eqs. (V.5-6), must be solved for complex values of Ta in order to examine growing wave solutions. A systematic examination of the solutions of such an equation would be a formidable task and is not undertaken here. The equation was derived only for completeness and to serve as a convenient point of departure for the work to follow.

If we allow the beam to fill the waveguide, (a = b), the complexity of the problem is reduced considerably. Considering the axially symmetric mode (n = 0) for this restricted case reduces Eq. (V.9) to

$$J_0(T_1 b) = 0, \qquad T_1 b = p_0 \nu \qquad \text{(V.10)}$$

where the $p_{0\nu}$'s are the ν roots of the Bessel function. Use of the definition of $T_1 b$ yields

$$p_{0\nu}^2 = -\beta b \; \frac{1 - \dfrac{\omega_p^2}{\omega^2} - \dfrac{(\beta_{pb} b)^2}{(\beta_e b - \beta b)^2}}{1 + \dfrac{\omega_p^2}{\omega_c^2 - \omega^2} + \dfrac{(\beta_{pb} b)^2}{(\beta_c b)^2 - (\beta_e b - \beta b)^2}} \qquad \text{(V.11)}$$

where

$\beta_e b = \omega b / u_0$ is the electronic or beam wave number

$\beta_c b = \omega_c b / u_0$ is the cyclotron wave number

$\beta_{pb} b = \omega_{pb} b / u_0$ is the beam plasma wave number

A few solutions of Eq. (V.11) have been obtained for typical values of the parameters. The rate of growth αb obtained from these solutions is plotted as a function of the electronic phase constant $\omega b / u_0$ in Fig. 24 for the first two circularly symmetric modes ($\nu = 1,2$). The perveance ($P = |I_0 / V_0^{3/2}|$, where I_0 is the dc beam current) and the ratio of operating frequency to plasma frequency are held constant. The fact that for $\beta_e b$

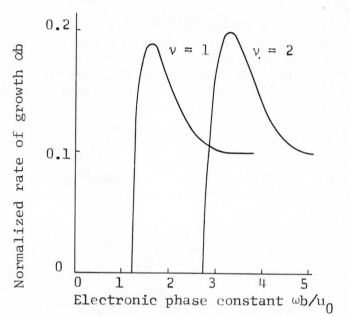

FIG. 24.--Rate of growth for the first two axially
    symmetric modes for interaction of elec-
    tron beam with stationary plasma column.
    Plasma and beam both filling cylindrical
    waveguide in infinite axial magnetic
    field. Microperveance, 1; $\omega/\omega_p = 0.5$.

below a certain value for a given axially symmetric
mode does not result in gain is explained by reference to the sketched ω-β diagrams for the first two
modes (Fig. 25) and by recognizing that the phase
velocity of the waves in the plasma must be nearly
in synchronism with the electron-beam velocity for
interaction to take place. Shown on this diagram
is a curve representing the electron beam velocity
u_0. As can be seen, increasing u_0 above the value
which corresponds to the phase velocity of the
waves ($u_0 > \omega_{pb}/p_{0\nu}$ for the plasma-filled waveguide in an infinite axial magnetic field) at low
frequencies results in no intersections of the ω-β
curve and the electron-beam velocity, as required

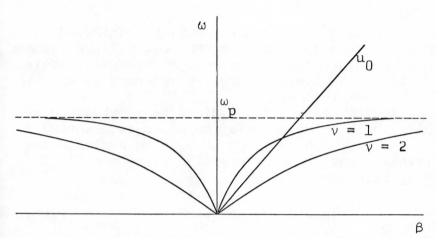

FIG. 25.--Sketch of phase characteristics for
         plasma-filled waveguide in infinite ax-
         ial magnetic field.

for interaction. This situation corresponds to
the minimum value of $\beta_e b$ of Fig. 24. On the other
hand, decreasing the beam velocity results in interaction with higher-order modes, since there are
intersections of the curve of dc beam velocity and
the ω-β curve for these higher modes. Increasing
the plasma frequency also results in interaction
with higher-order modes for a fixed beam velocity.
This result is understood by observing that the
points on the ω-β curves for the plasmaguide waves
are scaled upward when the plasma frequency is increased, which results in an intersection of the
ω-β curve with the dc beam velocity curve.

        APPROXIMATE ANALYSIS OF ELECTRON-BEAM PLASMA-
GUIDE INTERACTION. Pierce shows that the rate of
growth for the waves on an electron beam in the
presence of a slow-wave circuit can be calculated
approximately in terms of an interaction impedance
which is a measure of the electric field available
to act on the electrons for a given power flow on
the circuit.[14] Such an analysis can include the
effects of the space charge of the electron beam.

The effects of space charge will be neglected in
this analysis and the electron beam will be assumed
to be concentrated on the axis of symmetry. This
simplified analysis is usually referred to as a
"thin beam" theory.

Regarding the plasmaguides as slow-wave circuits permits the calculation of an interaction
impedance, which can then be used to evaluate the
traveling-wave-tube interaction parameter.[14] The
interaction impedance

$$K = E_{1z}^2 (0) / 2\beta^2 \overline{P}_z \qquad (V.12)$$

enters in the traveling-wave-tube interaction
parameter C by

$$C^3 = KI_0 / 4V_0 \qquad (V.13)$$

and $\overline{P}_z$ is the time average z-directed power flow
associated with the plasmaguide waves. From the
expression for power flow (Eq. III.48), the interaction impedance on the axis for a plasma-filled
waveguide in a finite magnetic field is given by

$$K = \frac{1}{\pi \epsilon_0 a} \left[\frac{(\omega_c^2 - \omega^2)}{(\omega_p^2 + \omega_c^2 - \omega^2)(\omega_p^2 - \omega^2)} \right]^{1/2} \frac{1}{p_{0v} J_1^2 (p_{0v})}$$

$$(V.14)$$

This expression is plotted in Fig. 26 as a function
of frequency. The impedance is seen to be zero
when $\omega = \omega_c$ (except when $\omega_p = \omega_c$), and infinite
when $\omega = \omega_p$ or $(\omega_p^2 + \omega_c^2)^{1/2}$.

It is of interest to compare the rate of
growth as predicted by the interaction impedance
calculation with that predicted by the field analysis. Consider the following operating conditions.

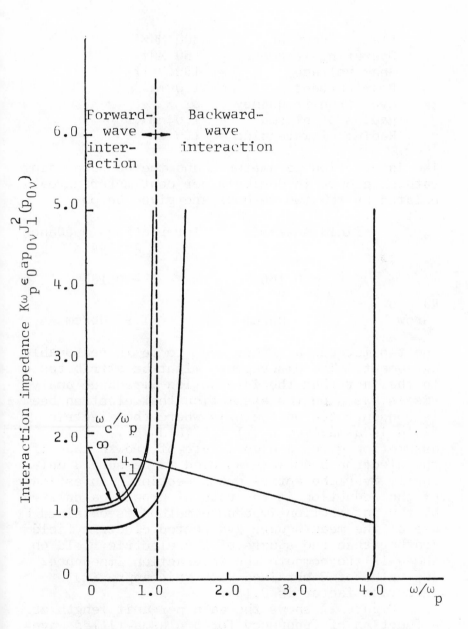

FIG. 26.--Interaction impedance for plasma-filled
         waveguide.

> Plasma frequency   =   300 MHz
> Operating frequency =   150 MHz
> Beam voltage   =   130 Volts
> Beam current   =   1.0 mA
> Cyclotron frequency =   ∞
> Radius of plasma   =   1.0 cm
> Radius of waveguide =   1.0 cm

The interaction parameter C and the corresponding
rate of growth in decibels per centimeter as calculated by the two methods are given below:

Field Analysis	Interaction-Impedance Analysis
$C = 0.166$	$C = 0.187$

	Field Analysis	Interaction-Impedance Analysis
Rate of Growth	1.73 db/cm	1.95 db/cm

The two methods are thus seen to be in reasonable
agreement. The discrepancy might be attributed
to the fact that the interaction impedance analysis is based on the assumption that electron beam
is concentrated on the axis where the electric
field is a maximum $E_z(r) = E_z(0) J_0(\beta r)$. This
assumption gives a higher rate of growth than if
the electron beam were assumed to be spread uniformly over the entire cross section. An estimate
of the reduction in the rate of growth calculated
by the interaction-impedance method is obtained by
use of the mean-square z-directed electric field
(rather than the square of the electric field on
the axis) to compute the interaction impedance.
The value of C obtained with this approximate
reduction factor is 0.134.

Figure 27 shows the gain per unit length as
a function of frequency for a plasma-filled waveguide of 1 cm diameter in an infinite axial magnetic field with a 0.5-mA electron beam on the

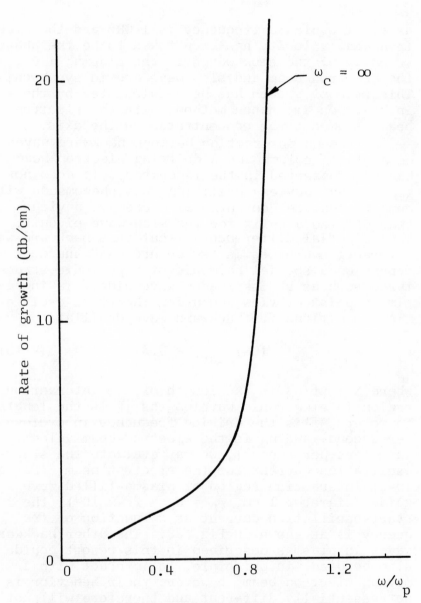

FIG. 27.--Rate of growth for electron beam in
        plasma-filled waveguide in infinite axial
        magnetic field. Electron beam velocity is
        synchronous with phase velocity of waves.
        Beam current, 0.5 mA; plasma frequency,
        1 GHz; plasma diameter, 1 cm.

axis. The plasma frequency is 1 GHz and the electron beam velocity has been taken to be the phase
velocity of the slow waves in the plasma; i.e.,
the electron beam and slow wave are in synchronism.
This rate of growth has been calculated by the
interaction impedance method, with the electron
beam assumed to be concentrated on the axis.

Although interaction between backward waves
on a plasma column and a drifting electron beam
has been observed in the laboratory, it does not
appear that devices utilizing this phenomenon will
come to replace conventional microwave devices
that utilize a helix for the slow-wave circuit.
The essential difference is that this backward-wave
interaction process is "structureless" and does not
depend on a spatial harmonic of a periodic structure, such as a disk-loaded waveguide. Taking a
simple point of view and using the start-oscillation conditions for backward wave oscillation,[26]

$$(CN)_{start} = 0.314 \qquad\qquad (V.15)$$

where $N = Lf/u_0$ is the length of the interaction
region in electronic wavelengths (L is the length
in meters, f is the driving frequency in cycles
per second, and u_0 is the electron-beam velocity
in meters per second), we may evaluate the start-
oscillation current for the electron beam. For a
10-cm interaction region of plasma-filled wave-
guide (diameter 1 cm, $\omega_p = \omega_c = 2\pi \times 10^9$), the
start-oscillation current as a function of fre-
quency is as shown in Fig. 28. The other backward
waves in plasmas described in this report could
also be used, in principle, to interact with a
moving electron beam; however, their behavior is
not essentially different and therefore will not
be examined here.

The expression for the interaction impedance
of Eq. (V.15) is not suitable for an examination

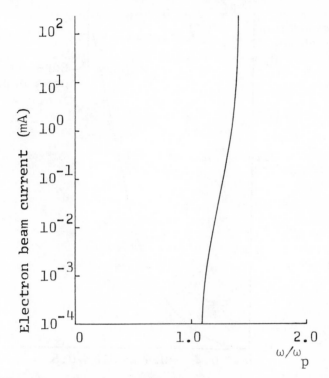

FIG. 28.--Start oscillation current for plasma-
        filled cylindrical waveguide. Inter-
        action region, 10 cm; plasma diameter,
        1 cm; $\omega_p = \omega_c = 2\pi 10^9$.

of the interaction of an electron beam with the
surface waves (see Chap. IV) since that expression
is for a plasma-filled waveguide where there is no
surface-wave propagation. Although the case of a
plasma only partially filling a waveguide in a
finite magnetic field could be examined for surface-wave electron-beam interaction, it is simpler
and no less instructive to consider a plasma
column in free space. The interaction impedance
of Eq. (V.12) is evaluated, with use of the expression for power flow, Eq. (IV.52):

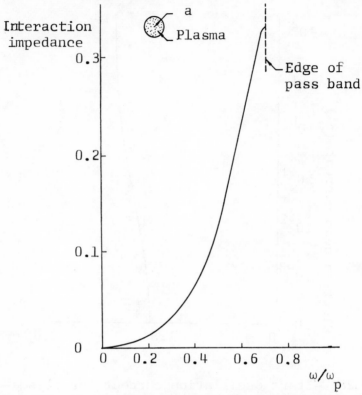

FIG. 29.--Interaction impedance for plasma column
            in free space.

$$K = \frac{1}{\omega_p \epsilon_0 \pi a}\left[\left(\frac{\omega}{\omega_p}\right)(\beta a)\left(1 - \frac{\omega_p^2}{\omega^2}\right)\left(\frac{I_1^2}{I_0^2} - \frac{I_2}{I_0}\right)\right.$$

$$\left. - \left(\frac{K_1^2}{K_0^2} - \frac{K_2}{K_0}\right)\right]^{-1} \qquad (V.16)$$

where the modified Bessel functions are of argument βa. The dimensionless interaction impedance
from Eq. (V.16) is plotted in Fig. 29 as a

function of ω/ω_p. The gain (in db/cm), for the
same operating conditions (beam current, 0.5 mA;
plasma diameter, 1 cm; plasma frequency, 1 GHz;
cyclotron frequency, zero; electron beam velocity
and phase velocity appropriate to operating frequency) as used in the infinite-magnetic-field
gain calculation, is shown in Fig. 30 as a function
of frequency.

The present analysis is not intended to be a
complete study of the interaction of electron beams
with stationary plasmas, but rather was included to
demonstrate that the slow waves which propagate on
a plasma column may interact with an electron beam
to produce growing waves, and to show that this
interaction can be achieved with plasmas and electron beams that are available in the laboratory.
The most important implication of this analysis
is that the backward-wave interaction could be
used to generate frequencies in the millimeter
range or to investigate the properties of plasmas
whose densities correspond to plasma frequencies
in the millimeter range. The usefulness of these
calculations is primarily that of demonstrating
the method of obtaining quantitative results for
plasma-beam interactions by regarding the plasma
as a slow-wave circuit and evaluating the interaction impedance.

ENERGY CONSERVATION IN PLASMAGUIDE WAVES. To
obtain the propagation characteristics of the plasmaguide modes, it was assumed that the ac magnetic
field could be neglected. To obtain an estimate
of the ac magnetic fields for power-flow calculations, it was assumed that they were not zero and
that they were given by $\nabla \times H = j\omega\bar{\bar{\epsilon}} \cdot E$. A demon-
stration that the power flow thus obtained is con-
sistent with the initial approximation can be
given by computing the time-average total stored
energy in the plasmaguide and multiplying by the
rate at which energy propagates in the system

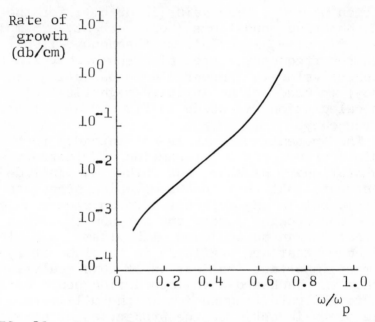

FIG. 30.--Rate of growth for electron beam interacting with the surface waves on plasma
column. Beam velocity is equal to phase
velocity of waves. Beam current, 0.5 mA;
plasma frequency, 1 GHz; plasma diameter,
1 cm.

(group velocity).

An expression for the total stored energy
can be derived from the differential form of
Poynting's theorem,

$$\nabla \cdot (\underline{E}_1 \times \underline{H}_1) + \frac{\partial}{\partial t} \left(\frac{\epsilon_0}{2} E_1^2 + \frac{\mu_0}{2} H_1^2 \right) + \underline{E}_1 \cdot \underline{J}_1 = 0$$

$$(V.17)$$

where $\underline{E}_1 \times \underline{H}_1$ is the Poynting vector and $(\epsilon_0/2) E_1^2$
and $(\mu_0/2) H_1^2$ are respectively the electric and
magnetic energy densities, and $\underline{E}_1 \cdot \underline{J}_1$ is the rate
at which the electrons extract energy from the
field. We evaluate $\underline{E}_1 \cdot \underline{J}_1$ from the equation of

motion

$$\frac{\partial \underline{v}_1}{\partial t} = - \frac{e}{m} \underline{E}_1 \qquad (V.18)$$

where either infinite or zero magnetic field has been assumed, and from the current $\underline{J}_1 = \rho_0 \underline{v}_1$; thus

$$\underline{E}_1 \cdot \underline{J}_1 = \left(\frac{m}{e}\right)^2 \frac{\epsilon_0}{2} \omega_p^2 \frac{\partial}{\partial t} v_1^2 \qquad (V.19)$$

The kinetic-power flow is zero and the kinetic energy density is

$$W_k = \left(\frac{m}{e}\right)^2 \frac{\epsilon_0}{2} \omega_p^2 v_1^2 \qquad (V.20)$$

Neglecting the magnetic energy density, we obtain for the time-average total stored energy per unit length

$$\overline{W}_T = \frac{\epsilon_0}{4} \, \text{Re} \int_S [E_1^2 + (m/e)^2 \omega_p^2 v_1^2] ds \qquad (V.21)$$

where S is the guide cross section. When the dc axial magnetic field is infinite, Eq. (V.21) becomes (for the plasma-filled guide of radius a, with the field components as given in Chap. III),

$$\overline{W}_T = \frac{\pi \epsilon_0}{2} A^2 (Ta)^2 J_1^2 (Ta) \frac{\omega_p^2/\omega^2}{(\omega_p/\omega)^2 - 1} \qquad (V.22)$$

where A is the excitation amplitude. The time-average power flow is given by

$$\overline{P}_z = v_g \overline{W}_T \tag{V.23}$$

where

$$v_g = \frac{\omega^2}{\omega_p^2} \frac{\omega}{\beta} \left(\frac{\omega_p^2}{\omega^2} - 1 \right) \tag{V.24}$$

is the group velocity. Thus,

$$\overline{P}_z = \frac{\epsilon_0 \pi A^2}{2} \frac{\omega}{\beta} (Ta)^2 J_1^2 (Ta) \tag{V.25}$$

which is the same as the power flow calculated by integrating Poynting's vector over the guide cross section, Eq. (III.48). The agreement of these two methods indicates that the approximate values for the ac magnetic field obtained with the quasistatic approximation are probably close to the actual magnetic field.

ATTENUATION OF PLASMAGUIDE WAVES. When the plasma electrons are produced by an electrical discharge in a gas, attenuation may arise because of collisions of the electrons with neutral gas molecules, positive ions, or the wall of the discharge tube. These collisions interrupt interaction with the wave and remove energy from it. An approximate way of including this effect is to define an average electron collision frequency ν_c and replace ω by $\omega - j\nu_c$ in the preceding equations. An approximate solution to these equations is obtained by writing

$$\alpha (\omega, \nu_v) + j\beta (\omega, \nu_c) \approx j\beta (\omega, 0) + j \frac{d\beta (\omega, 0)}{d\omega} (-j\nu_c) + \cdots \tag{V.26}$$

When ν_c is small the first two terms give a satisfactory approximation:

$$\alpha(\omega, \nu_c) = \frac{d\beta}{d\omega} \nu_c \qquad\qquad (V.27)$$

$$\beta(\omega, \nu_c) = \beta(\omega, 0) \qquad\qquad (V.28)$$

Thus to a first approximation the phase velocity
is unaffected by collisions and the attenuation
is proportional to the collision frequency and
inversely proportional to group velocity $d\omega/d\beta$.

6

relation of plasmaguide modes to space-charge waves on drifting electron beams

IT IS USUALLY ASSUMED that a drifting motion is essential to the propagation of energy by space-charge waves. That is actually true only for the case of a one-dimensional electron beam and does not apply for finite electron beams. The term "plasmaguide" has been used in the present treatment to denote the various electromechanical modes of propagation in stationary ion ion-neutralized plasma columns of finite cross section. These modes of propagation are the same as space-charge waves that would be seen by an observer in a coordinate system moving with the electron beam. A knowledge of the propagation characteristics in a system where the electrons are at rest can be used to investigate the properties of space-charge waves on a moving electron beam by means of a coordinate transformation. If ω and β are the frequency and propagation constants in the coordinate system where the electrons are at rest, the frequency ω' and propagation constant β' in the coordinate system where the electrons drift with velocity u_0 are

$$\omega' = \omega + \beta u_0 \qquad\qquad \text{(VI.1)}$$

$$\beta' = \beta \qquad\qquad \text{(VI.2)}$$

The wavelengths are the same; ω' is just the Doppler shifted frequency. Although each of the plasmaguide solutions given in the previous chapters can be easily modified to include a drift velocity, only the plasma-filled guide in an infinite magnetic field will be considered here. A typical ω-β diagram constructed from Fig. 1 with

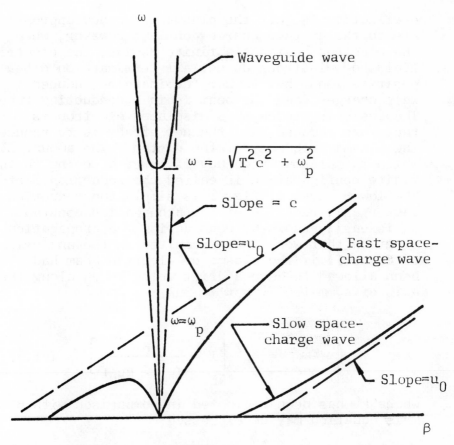

$$\omega \approx \sqrt{T^2 c^2 + \omega_p^2}$$

Slope $= c$

Slope$=u_0$

$\omega = \omega_p$

Waveguide wave

Fast space-charge wave

Slow space-charge wave

Slope$=u_0$

FIG. 31.--Phase characteristics of waves in elec-
        tron beam of velocity u_0 in infinite
        magnetic field.

the aid of Eqs. (VI.1-2) is shown in Fig. 31.
The slanted dashed lines are the phase characteristics of the one-dimensional or beam-of-infinite-
radius space-charge-wave solutions (see Eqs. I.6-7).
The departure from the one-dimensional solution
when the beam is small can be explained as follows.
When the electron-beam radius is infinite, all the
electric fields from the electrons terminate on
positive ions and the natural frequency of

oscillation is just the plasma frequency appropriate to the average charge density; however, when
the electron beam has a finite radius, the electric
fields of electrons do not all terminate on other
positive ions, but rather terminate on induced
wall charges when the beam is in a conducting tube.
The restoring force on a displaced electron is
therefore reduced, and the net effect is to reduce
the plasma frequency of the system. The amount by
which the plasma frequency is lowered owing to the
finite configuration is called the reduction factor.
The lower curve of Fig. 1 is simply the reduction
factor as a function of the propagation constant,
as is easily shown by considering the propagation
equation that would have resulted in the analysis
of Chap. II if the plasma or electron beam had
been allowed to have a drift velocity u_0 along the
axis of symmetry ($\omega = \omega' - \beta u_0$):

$$\left(\frac{p_{n\nu}}{a}\right)^2 = -\beta^2 \left[1 - \frac{\omega_p^2}{(\omega' - \beta u_0)^2}\right] \qquad (VI.3)$$

where k^2 has been neglected in comparison with β^2.
This equation may be expressed

$$\beta = \frac{\omega'}{u_0} \pm \frac{1}{[1 - (p_{n\nu}/\beta a)^2]^{1/2}} \frac{\omega_p}{u_0} \qquad (VI.4)$$

Comparing this result with Eq. (I.7) shows that
the reduction factor is

$$R = \frac{1}{[1 - (p_{n\nu}/\beta a)^2]^{1/2}} \qquad (VI.5)$$

which when solved for β/T ($T = p_{n\nu}/a$) yields

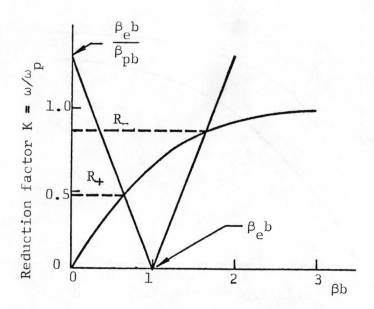

FIG. 32.--Diagram showing method for obtaining
           fast and slow space-charge waves from
           plasma mode phase characteristics.

$$\frac{\beta}{T} = \left(\frac{1}{R^2} - 1\right)^{-1/2} \qquad \text{(VI.6)}$$

By identifying R with ω/ω_p and comparing this
equation with the propagation equation we see
that the ω-β diagram for the propagation of space-
charge disturbances in coordinate systems where
the electrons are at rest is just the space-charge
reduction-factor curve (provided the ordinate is
measured in units of ω/ω_p). A simple graphical
method[27] for obtaining the reduction factors of
the fast and slow space-charge waves in terms of
$\beta_e a = \omega a/u_0$ can be given by plotting

$$\beta a = \beta_e a \pm R_{\pm} \beta_p a \qquad \text{(VI.7)}$$

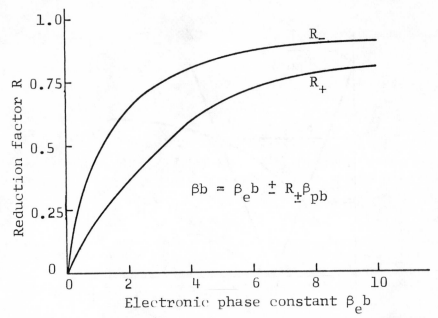

FIG. 33.--Fast and slow space-charge-wave reduction
factors for ion-neutralized electron beam
filling drift tube. Cyclotron frequency
equal to plasma frequency ($\beta_{pb} = 1$).

on the plasmaguide ω-β diagram when it is plotted
as ω/ω_p as a function of βa (Fig. 32). The intersections of the ω-β curve and the curves of Eq.
(VI.7) represent the solutions, the value of ω/ω_p
being just the reduction factor for a beam in that
configuration having the value of $\beta_e a$ selected to
plot Eq. (VI.7). Considering many values of $\beta_e a$
allows the fast and slow space-charge wave reduction factors (R_+ and R_-, respectively) to be plotted
as a function of the beam propagation constant
β_e. The curves thus obtained do not include the
usual approximation made in investigating space-
charge waves, namely that $\omega_p \ll \omega$. A typical reduction-factor curve obtained from this method is
shown in Fig. 33.
        In summary, we have shown the relation of

plasmaguide waves to the space-charge waves on a drifting electron beam. The method of obtaining the moving-beam reduction factors described here is much simpler than that of solving the field equations including the drifting motion of the electron beam. Thus the properties of space-charge waves for many cases can be determined by solving Poisson's equation in a system where the electrons do not have a drift velocity and transferring to a coordinate system where the electrons have the desired drift velocity.

slow-wave propagation in ferrite waveguides

IN CHAP. III IT WAS SHOWN that for a plasma-filled waveguide in a finite axial dc magnetic field the necessary condition for propagation was that the ratio of the zz-component of the dielectric tensor for the plasma to the rr-component must be negative:

$$T^2 = -\beta^2 \frac{\epsilon_{zz}}{\epsilon_{rr}} \qquad [\text{III.21}]$$

for the reason that T^2 is greater than zero and for propagating waves β^2 must be positive. For a ferrite-filled waveguide in a finite axial magnetic field, a region exists in which the zz-component and the rr-component of the permeability tensor are of opposite sign, and it seems quite likely that a "magnetic dual" to the plasmaguide waves should exist.

FERRITE ROD IN A CYLINDRICAL WAVEGUIDE. Consider a perfectly conducting cylindrical waveguide of radius b containing a homogeneous lossless ferrite rod of radius a, and let there be a finite axial magnetic field B_0. The ferrite will be treated as an anisotropic medium of tensor permeability[11]

$$\underline{\underline{\mu}} = \mu_0 \begin{Vmatrix} \mu_{rr} & -j\mu_{r\theta} & 0 \\ +j\mu_{\theta r} & \mu_{\theta\theta} & 0 \\ 0 & 0 & \mu_{zz} \end{Vmatrix} \qquad (VII.1)$$

where

$$\mu_{rr} = \mu_{\theta\theta} = 1 - \frac{\sigma P}{1 - \sigma^2} \qquad \text{(VII.2)}$$

$$\mu_{r\theta} = \mu_{\theta r} = \frac{P}{1 - \sigma^2} \qquad \text{(VII.3)}$$

$$\mu_{zz} = 1 \qquad \text{(VII.4)}$$

and

$$P = |\gamma| \frac{M_0}{\mu_0} \frac{1}{\omega} \qquad \text{(VII.5)}$$

$$\sigma = |\gamma| H_0 \frac{1}{\omega} \qquad \text{(VII.6)}$$

where M_0 is the dc magnetization, H_0 is the dc magnetic intensity, and γ is the gyromagnetic ratio for the electron. The variation of components of the permeability tensor is sketched in Fig. 34.[*]
     To study the propagation characteristics of this system the quasistatic approximation will again be used. In this case, however, it will be the ac electric field which will be neglected. Unfortunately a situation analogous to the infinite-magnetic-field case for the plasma-filled guide (Chap. II) that can be treated simply and rigorously does not seem to exist. The validity of the approximation here will have to rest on making a test of the solutions to see if the ac electric field components are negligible. Setting the ac electric field equal to zero in the curl B Maxwell equation,

$$\nabla \times \underline{H}_1 = j\omega\epsilon\underline{E}_1 \qquad \text{(VII.7)}$$

[*]This sketch is taken from Ref. 11.

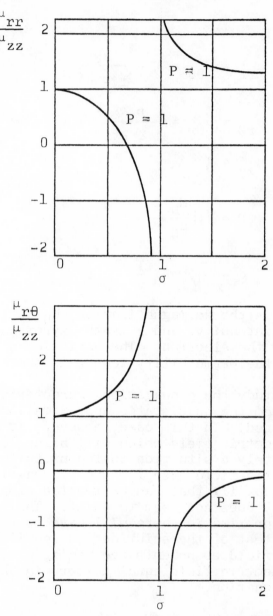

FIG. 34.--Relative radial and angular permeabilities
'for ferrite rod in axial magnetic field.

permits the magnetic intensity to be derived from
a scalar potential

$$\underline{H}_1 = -\nabla \emptyset_1 \qquad\qquad (VII.8)$$

where the differential equation to be satisfied
by $\emptyset_1$ comes from the requirement

$$\nabla \cdot \underline{B}_1 = \nabla \cdot (\underline{\underline{\mu}} \cdot \underline{H}_1) = 0 \qquad (VII.9)$$

Using the tensor permeability given in Eq. (VII.1)
leads to the following partial differential
equation:

$$\frac{1}{r}\frac{\partial}{\partial r}(r\mu_{rr}H_{1r} - j\mu_{r\theta}H_{1\theta}) + \frac{1}{r}\frac{\partial}{\partial \theta}(j\mu_{\theta r}H_{1r} + \mu_{\theta\theta}H_{1\theta})$$

$$+ \frac{\partial}{\partial z}(\mu_{zz}H_{1z}) = 0 \qquad\qquad (VII.10)$$

The partial differential equation in the magnetostatic potential is

$$\frac{1}{r}\frac{\partial}{\partial r}\left(r\frac{\partial}{\partial r}\emptyset_1\right) + \frac{1}{r^2}\frac{\partial^2\emptyset_1}{\partial\theta^2} + \frac{\mu_{zz}}{\mu_{rr}}\frac{\partial^2\emptyset_1}{\partial z^2} = 0 \quad (VII.11)$$

Assuming wave solutions

$$\emptyset_1 = K(r)e^{-jn\theta}e^{-j\beta z} \qquad\qquad (VII.12)$$

leads to the following differential equation,
which must be satisfied by the radial function:

$$\frac{1}{r}\frac{d}{dr}\left(r\frac{dR}{dr}\right) - \frac{n^2}{r^2}R - \beta^2\frac{\mu_{zz}}{\mu_{rr}}R = 0 \quad \text{(VII.13)}$$

Let $\qquad T^2 = -\beta^2\,\mu_{zz}/\mu_{rr}$ $\qquad\qquad\qquad$ (VII.14)

Then the solutions of Bessel's differential equation (VII.19) are

$$R(r) = AJ_n(Tr) + BN_n(Tr) \qquad \text{(VII.15)}$$

The second solution is singular at the origin and may be omitted. Suitable solutions for the potential inside the ferrite and the associated field components are:

$$\emptyset_{1i}(r,\theta,z,t) = AJ_n(Tr) \qquad\qquad\qquad \text{(VII.16)}$$

$$H_{1r}(r,\theta,z,t) = -ATJ_n'(Tr) \qquad\qquad\quad \text{(VII.17)}$$

$$H_{1\theta}(r,\theta,z,t) = A\,\frac{jn}{r}\,J_n(Tr) \qquad\qquad\quad \text{(VII.18)}$$

$$H_{1z}(r,\theta,z,t) = Aj\beta J_n(Tr) \qquad\qquad\qquad \text{(VII.19)}$$

$$e^{j(\omega t - n\theta - \beta z)}, \quad r < a$$

The solution outside the ferrite is obtained by setting $\mu_{rr} = \mu_{zz} = 1$ in (VII.13):

$$\emptyset = C[\,I_n(\beta r)K_n'(\beta b) - I_n'(\beta b)K_n(\beta r)\,]e^{j(\omega t - n\theta - \beta z)}$$

$$a < r < b \qquad\qquad\qquad \text{(VII.20)}$$

This solution satisfies the boundary condition that the normal component of the ac magnetic induction must vanish at the wall of the conducting waveguide. One of the boundary conditions at the surface of the ferrite rod, i.e., that the tangential component of the ac magnetic intensity must be continuous, is satisfied by taking

$$A = [J_n(Ta)]^{-1} \qquad \text{(VII.21)}$$

$$B = [I_n(\beta a)K_n'(\beta b) - I_n'(\beta b)K_n(\beta a)]^{-1} \quad \text{(VII.22)}$$

The other boundary condition, that the normal component of the ac magnetic induction must be continuous, leads to the equation for propagation of waves in this system,

$$\mu_{rr}(Ta) \frac{J_n'(Ta)}{J_n(Ta)} + n\mu_{r\theta}$$

$$= (\beta a) \frac{I_n'(\beta b)K_n'(\beta b) - I_n'(\beta b)K_n'(\beta a)}{I_n(\beta a)K_n'(\beta b) - I_n'(\beta b)K_n(\beta a)} \quad \text{(VII.23)}$$

As discussed in Chap. III, the fact that Eq. (VII.23) is an odd function of n indicates that the value of β for +n is different from -n, resulting in the rotation of the plane of polarization of a linearly polarized wave (for this case slow-wave Faraday rotation). Since the present treatment is primarily concerned with wave propagation in plasma-filled waveguides, a systematic examination of the properties of slow-wave propagation in ferrites will not be given; however, it is of interest to examine at least one case and obtain the ω-β diagram.

FERRITE-FILLED WAVEGUIDE IN FINITE AXIAL DC MAGNETIC FIELD. When the ferrite fills the guide (b = a), the numerator of the right side of

Eq. (VII.32) vanishes and the propagation equation is

$$(Ta) \frac{J_n'(Ta)}{J_n(Ta)} = -n \frac{\mu_{r\theta}}{\mu_{rr}} \qquad (VII.24)$$

In contrast with the plasma-filled guide, the ferrite-filled guide can produce a rotation of the plane of polarization of the higher-order modes $(n > 0)$. Again, the higher-order modes undoubtedly have interesting properties which could be systematically investigated; however, interest will be confined in this paper to the case of axially symmetric modes $(n = 0)$.

For the circularly symmetric mode $(n = 0)$,

$$J_1(Ta) = 0, \qquad Ta = p_{1\nu} \qquad (VII.25)$$

where $p_{1\nu}$ are the ν roots of the Bessel function of order unity. The normalized propagation constant can then be expressed

$$\left(\frac{\beta}{T}\right)^2 = -\frac{\mu_{rr}}{\mu_{zz}} \qquad (VII.26)$$

Examination of Fig. 34 reveals that there is a narrow frequency band just above the precession resonance where the quantity μ_{zz}/μ_{rr} on the right side of Eq. (VII.26) is negative. The ω-β diagram for this passband is shown in Fig. 35; as can be seen, the waves are backward waves.

A possible use of the ferrite modes would be that of measuring the properties of the ferrite. The technique would be similar to that described in Chap. VII for plasma diagnostics, i.e., by measuring the attenuation, it should be possible to deduce the losses in the ferrite, and by measuring the phase velocity versus frequency, it

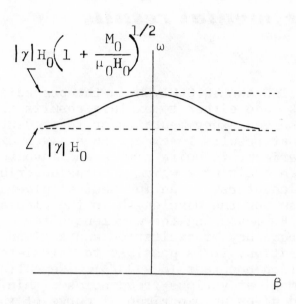

FIG. 35.--Phase characteristics for slow-wave pro-
        pagation in ferrite-filled cylindrical
        waveguide in axial magnetic field H_0
        (axially symmetric mode).

should be possible to establish the permeability
tensor components.

8

experimental results

MOST OF THE ANALYSIS GIVEN in the preceding chapters was made either to explain results that had
been observed experimentally or to predict in ad-
vance what results to expect in a given experiment.
The experiment is quite simple and involves nothing
more than exciting a wave, such as described in
earlier chapters, on an ion-neutral plasma column
and measuring the wavelength in the plasma waveguide. By measuring the wavelength for a particular frequency of excitation and a given
configuration, it is possible to calculate the
propagation constant $(\beta = 2\pi/\lambda)$. Repeating this
measurement at various frequencies within the
passband gives an experimental curve of the phase
characteristics of the waves $(\omega$ versus $\beta)$. Such
measurements were made and in each case the agreement between theory and experiment is quite good.
The experimental results will be presented in
relation to the analysis which is being verified.

DESCRIPTION OF EXPERIMENT. A schematic diagram of the apparatus used to investigate the properties of the various modes of propagation is
shown in Fig. 36. The plasma is the positive
column of a mercury-arc discharge that is main-
tained by applying a dc voltage (through a large
external resistor to limit the discharge current)
between the thermionic cathode and the anode.
The anode is a disk whose diameter is slightly
smaller than the diameter of the glass cylinder
that contains the plasma. The oxide-coated cathode
is a conventional type taken from a commercially
available mercury-arc rectifier tube. To excite
the waves in this system, a radio-frequency signal
is coupled to the plasma through the discharge

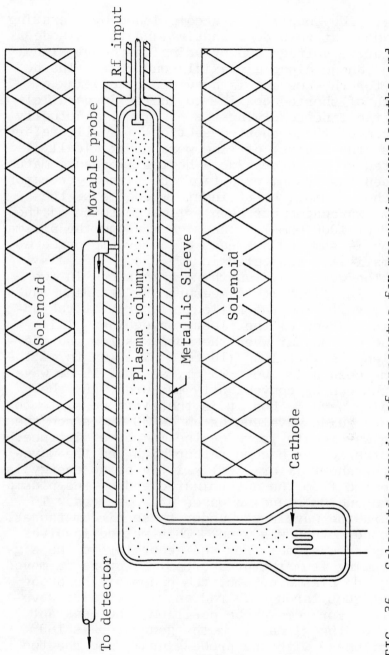

FIG. 36.--Schematic drawing of apparatus for measuring wavelengths and attenuation in plasma-filled waveguide.

anode. The coupling is accomplished by operating
the anode at zero dc potential and the cathode at
a negative voltage and by bringing the rf signal
to the anode along a coaxial conductor. The dc
path for the current is provided by placing a
length of shorted coaxial conductor in parallel
with the line supplying the rf signal. Actually,
several of these shorted sections (usually referred
to as stub tuners) of line were strategically
located so as to provide a better impedance match
between the 50-ohm output of the signal generator
and the plasma (the rf input impedance of the
plasma waveguide has been estimated to be of the
order of 1000 Ohms). The signal along the plasma
column is sampled by means of a movable probe as
schematically indicated in Fig. 36.

The guide wavelengths are measured in two
ways. The first is to measure the standing waves
that result from the reflected energy at the unterminated end of the plasma waveguide. This
method was useful when the loss was low and the
wavelengths were long (10 cm). The length of the
plasma column is about 25 cm, so that 15-cm wavelengths can be conveniently measured. By the
standing-wave method it is therefore possible to
measure guide wavelengths up to 30 cm, since the
guide wavelength is twice the measured distance.
When the losses become rather high and the wavelengths short (1 or 2 cm), little or no energy is
reflected from the unterminated end of the plasma
column and no standing waves are observed. To
measure the wavelength under these circumstances,
a second method was used. This method involves
adding some signal from the generator to the signal coming from the probe. As the probe is moved
along the plasma column, the phase of the probe
signal goes through 2π radians every guide wavelength. For some probe position, the constant
phase of the signal from the generator is 180°
out of phase with the probe signal, and the two

signals partially cancel. By adjusting the amplitude of the added signal, it is possible in principle to make the two signals cancel completely.
Thus as the probe is moved along the plasma column,
the combined output have minima at points that are
separated by one guide wavelength. The attenuation
of the signal with distance away from the input was
measured by observing the probe signal amplitude as
a function of probe position.

The pressure of the mercury within the tube
is controlled by regulating the temperature of a
mercury well which is attached to the glass en-
velope at a point near the cathode (not shown in
Fig. 36). The temperature is held between 26.7°
and 26.9°C (about 300°K), and the corresponding
pressure is a few microns. For this pressure,
the mean free path of the plasma electrons (a few
centimeters) is long compared with the diameter
of the discharge (0.328 in.). To make accurate
quantitative measurements, it would be essential
to immerse the entire discharge tube in a thermostatic bath. This would be a difficult procedure
from a practical standpoint and was not done because the experiments were not performed to provide accurate quantitative results, but rather to
verify the gross features of the waves reported in
the analysis. Although only the temperature of
the mercury well is regulated, the results are
quite reproducible, and it would seem that the
most serious consequence of only partial immersion
is to place all the results in error by a small
but constant amount.

Propagation was investigated from 10 to 4000
MHz. The cyclotron and plasma frequency are
variable over about the same range. The axial dc
magnetic field is provided by a solenoid. The
diameter of the plasma is 0.328 in. and the outer
diameter of the glass cylinder containing the
plasma is 0.410 in. One of the cylindrical waveguides in which the plasma column is placed

closely fits the glass cylinder, and the other
waveguide which is used in the experiment is
0.750 in. in diameter. When empty, the cutoff
frequencies for these waveguides are in the tens
of gigahertz, so that the frequencies used in the
experiment are all well below cutoff. The frequency range over which propagation was investigated was determined by the equipment available in
the laboratory and does not represent any fundamental limitation.

PLASMA COLUMN IN A CYLINDRICAL WAVEGUIDE:
FINITE MAGNETIC FIELD. In Chap. III it was shown
that the propagation characteristics depend on the
strength of the axial dc magnetic field. In addition to forward-wave passbands, there are backward-
wave passbands near the cyclotron or plasma
frequency, depending on which is larger. Figure 37
is a theoretical ω-β diagram for a plasma column
in a glass cylinder which tightly fits a cylindrical waveguide. Experimental points for several
discharge currents and magnetic fields are shown.
As can be seen the experimental points are in
agreement with the theoretical phase characteristics
Notice that in contrast with the presentation of
the phase characteristics in the theory sections
of this paper, the operating frequency is normalized to the cyclotron frequency rather than the
plasma frequency. The reason for this is that the
cyclotron frequency is known and until a comparison with the theory is made, the plasma frequency
is unknown. The backward-wave passbands are not
indicated in this diagram for the following reason:
using the cyclotron frequency as a normalizing frequency causes the backward-wave passbands to cross
the forward-wave passbands, creating a confusing
diagram. For another thing, no backward waves were
observed for this configuration of a tightly fitting metallic sleeve. The inability to observe the
backward waves is probably a result of high

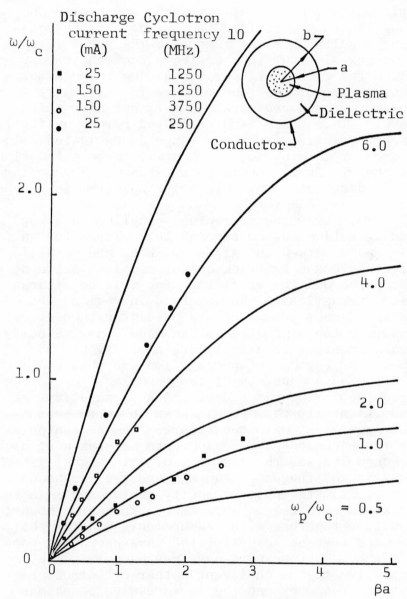

FIG. 37.--Theoretical phase characteristics for
plasma column in waveguide for finite
axial magnetic field and experimental
points; $\beta/a = 1.2$, $K_e = 4.62$.

attenuation, bad input mismatch, and poor probe
coupling to the rf fields. The poor probe coupling results from the fact that the probe is in
a narrow slot cut in the sleeve and can at most
touch the glass cylinder containing the plasma.
Another factor that contributes to difficulty in
observing backward waves is a rather high noise
level. This noise is distributed rather uniformly
over the entire frequency range investigated. The
source of this noise, which seems to be a function
of the rf signal level, is not known. A more complete description of this noise spectrum is given
in the next chapter.

        To remedy the poor probe coupling, a second
configuration was considered that allows for an
air space betwen the glass cylinder and metallic
sleeve, thus permitting better coupling between
the probe and the rf field. For this configuration, transmission was observed in regions where
backward-wave passbands are predicted theoretically;
however, the high attenuation made phase velocity
measurements virtually impossible. Figure 38
shows the regions of propagation for this configuration as a function of the normalized cyclotron
frequency. The range over which propagation was
experimentally observed is seen to be in reasonable agreement with the theory. The reason points
in the backward-wave region were not taken at higher
frequencies was the lack of suitable signal genera-
tors in the frequency range where the passbands
occur. Limited phase-velocity measurements in the
backward-wave region were made. They are shown in
Fig. 39, together with measurements made in the
forward-wave passband for the same operating conditions. The backward-wave passband is quite
sensitive to the choice of either cyclotron or
plasma frequency and the forward-wave passbands
are quite insensitive to small changes in these
quantities. The dashed phase characteristics curve
which best fits the experimental backward wave

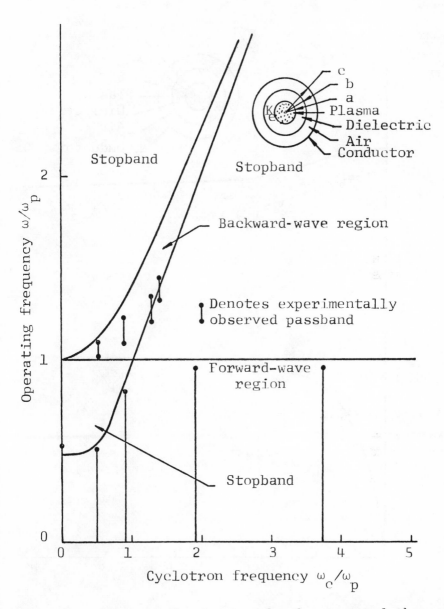

FIG. 38.--Diagram showing passbands expected theo-
           retically and regions where transmission
           was observed experimentally; c/b = 2,
           b/a = 1.2, K_e = 4.62.

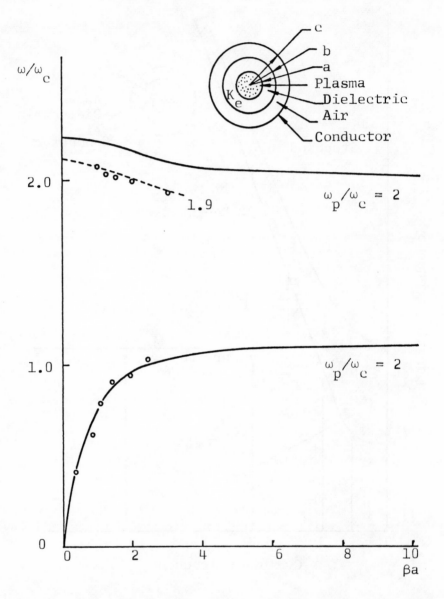

FIG. 39.--Theoretical phase characteristics for
        forward- and backward-wave passbands and
        experimental points corresponding approxi-
        mately to case shown; c/b = 2, b/a = 1.2,
        K_e = 4.62. Discharge current, 5mA;
        f_c = 250 MHz.

data is that for $\omega_p/\omega_c = 1.9$. As can be seen this
is rather far from the $\omega_p/\omega_c = 2$ curve for the
backward-wave passband. For the forward-wave
passband, however, the $\omega_p/\omega_c = 1.9$ curve is very
close to the $\omega_p/\omega_c = 2.0$ curve so that both would
fit the data equally well. For this reason,
$\omega_p/\omega_c = 1.9$ is probably the best value. Thus the
plasma frequency for this discharge current (5 ma)
is 475 MHz.

PLASMA COLUMN IN A CYLINDRICAL WAVEGUIDE:
ZERO MAGNETIC FIELD. In Chap. IV, the surface
waves that propagate on an isotropic plasma column
are discussed. To verify the features of these
modes, the same experimental set-up and technique
described earlier was used. The magnetic field of
the solenoid was reduced to zero. Figure 40 shows
the theoretical phase characteristics (for the configuration used in the experiment) that would result if the charge density were uniform over the
cross section of the tube. In Chap. IV it was
shown that if the charge density was a function of
radius (maximum on the axis and minimum at the
edge) the phase characteristics would be modified.
As can be seen from Fig. 40, the experimental
points for $\beta a > 1$ are below the uniform charge
density curve, which is as expected from the analysis. The experimental points are normalized to
the average charge density of the plasma column,
so that they all have the same behavior at low frequencies. The fact that their low-frequency phase
velocity depends only on the average charge density
is explained in Chap. IV. The experimental points
for the larger of the two discharge currents are
the lowest on the diagram. From the analysis of
Chap. IV, this result would indicate that the edge
charge density is lower relative to the axis charge
density for higher discharge currents. Such behavior can be explained qualitatively (1) by noting
that the rate of production of plasma electrons

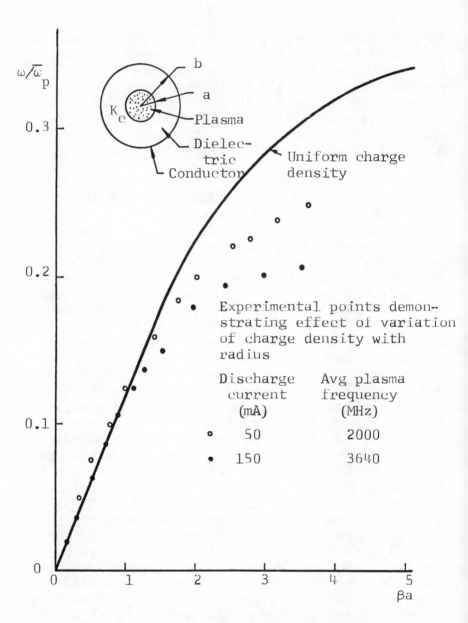

FIG. 40.--Theoretical phase characteristics for
         surface waves with experimental points;
         b/a = 1.2, K_e = 4.62.

increases with increasing discharge current and (2)
by assuming that the radial diffusion constant is
not a function of discharge current; i.e., that
the curvature of the distribution, which is proportional to the rate of production-diffusion constant ratio, increases with discharge current.
The value of the parameter α used in Chap. IV to
denote the parabolicity of the radial charge distribution has been calculated for a few cases;
however, the values are at best crude estimates
for reasons cited in Chap. IV and will therefore
not be given as results.

PLASMA DIAGNOSTICS. It was shown in Chap. IV,
in the section on the effect of variation of charge
density with radius, that the phase velocity at low
frequencies is asymptotic to a constant velocity
which depends on the average charge density and the
configuration. A measurement of this low-frequency
phase velocity therefore provides a measure of the
average plasma frequency. This was shown only for
the surface waves which exist in the absence of an
axial magnetic field. It is assumed, without
proof, that the low-frequency phase velocity of
waves which propagate in the presence of an axial
magnetic field also depends only on the average
charge density. Figure 41 shows curves of the
plasma frequency squared (proportional to average
charge density) as a function of the axial magnetic field for several discharge currents. As
the magnetic field is increased from zero, there
is a sharp enhancement of the average charge density. This result is explained by observing that
the plasma electrons go from a regime at zero magnetic field, where wall collision (the mean free
path of plasma electrons is several times the diameter of the glass cylinder containing the plasma)
is the primary loss mechanism, to a regime where
only a few electrons collide with the wall because
their cyclotron radius is much smaller than the

diameter of the plasma column. Thus at a magnetic
field greater than the value required for the cyclotron radius to equal the plasma column diameter
for electrons at a few volts, the plasma electrons
should drift along the axis of symmetry spending a
longer time in the plasma, which should lead to a
higher average charge density. It would be expected
that once the cyclotron radius was much smaller than
the diameter of the plasma column that a further
increase of the magnetic field would produce no
further enhancement of the charge density. As
seen in Fig. 41, this expectation is in agreement
with the experimental observation.

Equation (V.33) relates the average collision
frequency of plasma electrons to the wave attenuation along the plasma column and simultaneous
evaluation of the group velocity therefore provides a measure of the collision frequency. Figure 42 is a plot of the collision frequency as a
function of discharge current for zero axial magnetic field. The measured collision frequency is
in agreement with a calculation based on a few
volts of energy for plasma electrons and a mean
free path long compared with the 1-cm diameter
(the calculated collision frequency is the order
of 100 MHz). Attenuation measurements in the presence of an axial magnetic field have been made.
The loss was in most cases low and reflected energy
from the end of the plasma column prevented accurate measurements. The results are questionable
and will not be included.

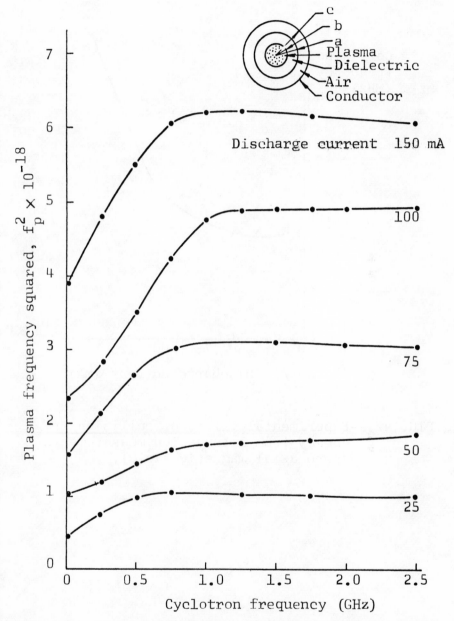

FIG. 41.--Plasma frequency as function of magnetic
        field for several discharge currents;
        c/b = 2, b/a = 1.2, K_e = 4.62.

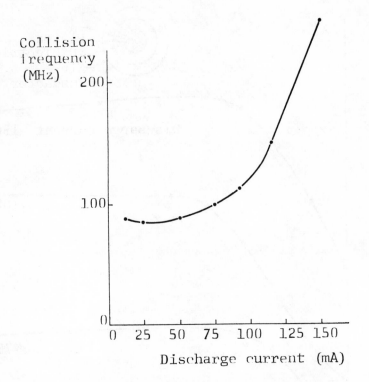

FIG. 42.--Experimental values of collision frequency from attenuation measurements
(zero axial magnetic field).

summary and conclusions

9

SOME OF THE FEATURES OF slow electromechanical
modes of wave propagation in a stationary plasma
of finite transverse cross section have been examined by considering the plasma to be a dielectric
and solving the field equations. It has been
shown that two basic types of propagation exist,
both of which have phase velocities that are generally much less than the velocity of light. The
first might be described as a body wave since it
involves a perturbation in the average charge
density of the plasma; the presence of a dc magnetic field is essential to the existence of body
waves. The second is a surface wave which involves
a perturbation or "rippling" of the plasma surface
but no charge accumulation within the plasma; this
type exists for either zero or small dc magnetic
fields and does not exist when the plasma completely
fills a conducting waveguide. Each of these types
of propagation has modes that can exist down to
zero frequency and modes which for certain conditions are <u>backward</u> waves. Backward waves usually
exist as a spatial harmonic on a periodic circuit
and not as separate and distinct modes as observed
here. Five distinct backward waves are reported
and the possibility of interacting an electron
beam with one of them is considered briefly. The
interaction of an electron beam with this "structureless" backward wave has potential application
in the generation of very high microwave frequencies
since the emphasis would be shifted from the fabrication of delicate slow-wave structures to that of
obtaining plasmas of very high charge density.
Faraday rotation of the plane of polarization was
an important consideration in the perturbation of
the electromagnetic waveguide modes by the

introduction of a plasma into the waveguide system.
Significant Faraday rotation is shown to exist for
the angular-dependent slow-wave modes in a plasma
column partially filling a conducting waveguide in
a finite axial dc magnetic field. It is shown that
it is not essential for the dc magnetic field to be
coaxial with the waveguide system for propagation
to exist by considering the problem of a plasma-
filled rectangular waveguide with a dc magnetic
field perpendicular to one of the guide surfaces.
The mode types which result are a backward wave
which propagates down to zero frequency and a
narrow-passband forward wave near the plasma
frequency.

The surface waves which involve no charge
accumulation within the plasma are quite sensitive
to the radial charge density variation of the plasma column near the edge of the passband. At low
frequencies, however, the phase velocities of the
waves depend only on the average charge density.
The effects of the radial charge density on the
propagation characteristic are examined and experimental methods for obtaining a measure of the
radial charge variation and the average charge
density are described. It seems likely that one
of the most useful applications of surface-wave
propagation is that of plasma diagnostics, since
the frequencies required are much lower than the
plasma frequency. This feature is of particular
interest where the charge densities correspond to
millimeter-wavelength plasma frequencies and signal generation is rather difficult. A measurement
of the attenuation of the wave amplitude is shown
to provide a measure of the average collision frequency in the plasma. This method could be quite
useful in obtaining the collision frequency in
regimes where an analytical solution would be
quite difficult.

Each of the modes described is closely related to space-charge waves associated with drifting

electron beams. A method for obtaining the properties of drifting electron-beam space-charge
waves by a coordinate transformation is described.
The space-charge-wave reduction factor for drifting
beams is easily obtained from the stationary plasma
phase characteristics by a simple graphical construction. This procedure makes it much easier to
obtain the space-charge-wave reduction factor as
well as providing a better understanding of the
nature of space-charge waves in general.

Slow-wave magnetostatic modes of propagation
in ferrite waveguides, which are essentially the
magnetic dual of the waves in a stationary plasma,
are examined briefly. These modes do not appear
to be too useful at the present time except for
purposes of ferrite diagnostics. The electric
fields associated with these modes are small and
the possibility of interaction of electron beams
with these modes seems unlikely. For an axial
magnetic field there is one slow backward-wave
passband near the precession resonance frequency,
and for a transverse magnetic field there is a
forward-wave passbnad in the same vicinity.

Many of the features of the plasma modes have
been verified experimentally by measuring the phase
velocity on a mercury-arc discharge column. These
measurements have yielded estimates of charge density which are in essential agreement with other
methods of obtaining charge density.

The analytical and experimental work reported
in this book does not pretend to be exhaustive;
in fact, more problems were uncovered that remain
to be solved than were solved. One of the more
interesting of these problems is the nature of the
noise which seriously hampered efforts to obtain
precise experimental data. This noise is present
both with and without magnetic fields. With magnetic fields there was a more or less continuous
spectrum with several discrete prominences for
which the amplitude of successive peaks was

lessened as the frequency was increased. For some
operating conditions, the amplitude of the noise
was a function of position along the guide. It
is not known whether these signals were growing or
decaying since their origin is not known. For
other conditions, there were definite standing
waves of noise voltage along the mercury discharge
column. In most cases the level of noise voltage
at any plane along the discharge column appeared
to be related to the level of the incident signal
(the noise increased as the signal level was
raised). One of the types of noise that is known
to exist in discharge columns is that of moving
striations, although it is not known to be the
mechanism in this case.

    Another interesting problem is that of slow-
wave propagation in discharges of the thermonuclear
type. The primary differences should come from
the rather large circumferential magnetic field
that results from the large currents carried by
the discharge. A knowledge of the properties of
these waves and experimental procedures similar to
those described in this paper should permit the
diagnostics of such discharges.

    The possibility of interacting an electron
beam with any of the backward waves described to
make a "structureless" backward-wave oscillator
is particularly intriguing. Although interaction
of an electron beam with one of the forward-wave
modes has been observed, the results were entirely
too preliminary to be reported in a systematic way.
Work is being continued in the hope that backward-
wave interaction will be found.

    Certain deviations from the theoretical sur-
face-wave behavior (which were not described in
the chapter on experimental work) can probably be
attributed to the variation in charge density near
the edge of the plasma column.

    The primary conclusion to be drawn from this
analysis is that a drifting motion of a plasma is

not essential to the propagation of space-charge-
wave disturbances provided that the plasma is of
finite transverse cross section. The most important result of the analysis is that of describing
methods whereby the properties of plasmas can be
investigated by rather simple experimental techniques involving frequencies which are much less
than the plasma frequency. Also of interest is
the conclusion or implication that the propagation
of noise disturbances near the potential minimum
of a diode may be considerably different from that
predicted by one-dimensional space-charge-wave
theory when the plasma frequency is of the same
order as the frequency of interest. Finally, it
seems likely that an understanding of these slow-
wave modes of propagation may be useful in studying
the radiation or reception of radio signals in
guided missiles since the hot exhaust gases are a
low-frequency propagating structure, and the an-
tenna pattern might be modified by the exhaust gas
column which forms part of the missile from the
rf viewpoint.

appendix I: one-dimensional space-charge waves

Consider an ion-neutralized, drifting electron stream of average velocity u_{0z} and average charge density ρ_0. A simple derivation for the space-charge waves which propagate in this system begins by assuming the total velocity and charge density to be the average value plus a small, harmonic time-dependent perturbation,

$$v(z,t) = u_{0z} + v_{1z} e^{j(\omega t - \beta z)} \tag{AI.1}$$

$$\rho(z,t) = \rho_0 + \rho_1 e^{j(\omega t - \beta z)} \tag{AI.2}$$

The total convection current density $J = \rho v$ passing a given plane is also assumed to have an average value plus a small perturbation,

$$J(z,t) = J_{0z} + J_{1z}(z,t) = \rho_0 u_{0z} + (u_{0z}\rho_1 + \rho_0 v_{1z})e^{j(\omega t - \beta z)} \tag{AI.3}$$

where the term $\rho_1 v_{1z}$ has been neglected since it is the product of perturbation quantities and is of second order. For the assumed time and space dependence, the ac current and ac charge density are related by the equation of continuity (II.8),

$$J_{1z} - (\omega/\beta)\rho_1 = 0 \tag{AI.4}$$

The ac electric field is related to the ac charge density by the divergence relation (II.3),

$$j\beta E_{1z} + (\rho_1/\epsilon_0) = 0 \tag{AI.5}$$

The ac velocity and ac electric field are related by the equation of motion (II.7),

$$(\omega - \beta u_{0z})v_{1z} - j \frac{e}{m} E_{1z} = 0 \tag{AI.6}$$

where

$$\frac{dv}{dt} = \frac{\partial v}{\partial t} + \frac{\partial v}{\partial z}\frac{dz}{dt} \approx \frac{\partial v}{\partial t} + u_{0z}\frac{\partial v}{\partial t}$$

since v is a function of both z and t. Taking $dz/dt = u_{0z}$ assumes the drift velocity to be much larger than the ac velocity. The ac convection current density from Eq. (AI.3) can be written as

$$J_{1z} - u_{0z}\rho_1 - \rho_0 v_{1z} = 0 \tag{AI.7}$$

Equations (AI.4-7) constitute a set of homogeneous algebraic equations which relate the ac velocity, charge density, current, and electric field. To have a nontrivial solution, the determinant of the coefficients associated with these variables must vanish. The interesting solution

$$\omega_p^2 - (\omega - \beta u_{0z})^2 = 0 \qquad\qquad\qquad (AI.8)$$

is the propagation equation for the space-charge waves associated with the drifting motion of the electron stream; $\omega_p^2 = -\rho_0 e/\epsilon_0 m$ is the electron plasma frequency. The implications of this equation are examined in the introduction (see I.1).

appendix II: admittance transformation

The characteristic equation for the propagation of waves in multiregion systems can be obtained by calculating the surface admittance (ratio of tangential H to tangential E when surface currents are absent) in two adjoining regions and equating them at the boundary. Birdsall shows that the surface admittance at a plane (or as in the case considered here, at some cylindrical surface) can be easily calculated by means of cutoff guide admittance transformation if the admittance is known at some other plane such as at the conducting wall of a waveguide.[28] This method need only be modified slightly to be used with the quasistatic approximation to obtain the propagation equation of a multiregion system containing a plasma column.

The boundary condition for the quasistatic approximation is continuity of the ratio of normal displacement to tangential electric field at each discontinuity. This ratio is presumed known at the conducting surface of the waveguide and can be transformed to the surface of the plasma column by successive application of the transformation through each region between the waveguide wall and the plasma surface. In each region outside the plasma, the phasor potential is

$$\emptyset_1 = AI_n(\beta r) + BK_n \beta r \tag{AII.1}$$

The normal displacement and tangential electric field are

$$\epsilon E_{1r} = -\epsilon \frac{\partial \emptyset_1}{\partial r} = -\epsilon\beta[AI_n'(\beta r) + BK_n'(\beta r)] \tag{AII.2}$$

$$E_{1z} = -\frac{\partial \emptyset_1}{\partial z} = + j\beta[AI_n(\beta r) + BK_n(\beta r)] \tag{AII.3}$$

We define a surface admittance

$$\epsilon \frac{E_{1r}}{E_{1z}} = jQ(x) = -\frac{1}{j}\epsilon \frac{AI_n'(x) + BK_n'(x)}{AI_n(x) + BK_n(x)} \tag{AII.4}$$

where the notation $x = \beta r$ has been used. At some other radius $(\beta r' = y)$,

$$Q(y) = \epsilon \frac{\frac{A}{B} I_n'(y) + K_n'(y)}{\frac{A}{B} I_n(y) + K_n(y)} \tag{AII.5}$$

Solving Eq. (AII.4) for the ratio of A/B and substituting in Eq. (AII.5) yields

$$Q(y) = \epsilon \frac{\epsilon[I_n'(y)K_n'(x) - I_n'(x)K_n'(y)] + Q(x)[I_n(x)K_n'(y) - I_n'(y)K_n(x)]}{\epsilon[I_n(y)K_n'(x) - I_n'(x)K_n(y)] + Q(x)[I_n(x)K_n(y) - I_n(y)K_n(x)]}$$

(AII.6)

This equation allows the evaluation of $Q(y)$ if $Q(x)$ and the values of x, y and the dielectric constant ϵ are given:

As an example, consider the three-region problem (i.e., plasma column of radius a filling a dielectric cylinder of outer radius b in a waveguide of radius c. Now $Q(\beta c)$ is infinite and $Q(\beta b)$ ($\beta b < \beta c$) is given by

$$Q(\beta b; \beta c, \epsilon_0) = \epsilon_0 \frac{[I_n(\beta c)K_n'(\beta b) - I_n'(\beta b)K_n(\beta c)]}{[I_n(\beta c)K_n(\beta b) - I_n(\beta b)K_n(\beta c)]}$$ (AII.7)

A second transformation from b to a gives the value of $Q(\beta a_+)$ just outside the plasma radius. Equating this to the value of $Q(\beta a_-)$ just inside the plasma radius gives

$$\left(1 - \frac{\omega_p^2}{\omega^2}\right) \frac{I_n'(\beta a)}{I_n(\beta a)}$$

$$= K_e \frac{K_e[I_n'(\beta a)K_n'(\beta b) - I_n'(\beta b)K_n'(\beta a)] + \frac{Q(\beta b)}{\epsilon_0}[I_n(\beta b)K_n'(\beta a) - I_n'(\beta a)K_n(\beta b)]}{K_e[I_n(\beta a)K_n'(\beta b) - I_n'(\beta b)K_n(\beta a)] + \frac{Q(\beta b)}{\epsilon_0}[I_n(\beta b)K_n(\beta a) - I_n(\beta a)K_n(\beta b)]}$$

(AII.8)

where $Q(\beta b)$ is given by Eq. (AII.7). Each of the quantities within the brackets in Eqs. (AII.7-8) are tabulated for a limited number of cases,[28] permitting numerical solutions to be obtained with relative ease.

appendix III

Reprinted from JOURNAL OF APPLIED PHYSICS, Vol. 30, No. 11, 1784–1793, November, 19

Space Charge Waves in Cylindrical Plasma Columns*

A. W. TRIVELPIECE† AND R. W. GOULD

California Institute of Technology, Pasadena, California

When a plasma is of finite transverse cross section, space-charge waves may propagate even in the absence of a drift motion or thermal velocities of the plasma. Some of the properties of these space charge waves have been investigated by regarding the plasma as a dielectric and solving the resulting field equations. The effect of a steady axial magnetic field is considered, but motion of heavy ions and electron temperature effects are neglected. Waves are found to exist at frequencies low compared with the plasma frequency as well as waves with oppositely directed phase and group velocities (backward waves).

Many of the features of these waves have been verified experimentally by measuring phase velocity and attenuation of waves along the positive column of a low pressure mercury arc in an axial magnetic field. Measurements of electron density have been made using these waves and the results are compared with those obtained by other methods. An interesting feature of these measurements, of value in plasma diagnostics, is that they can be made with frequencies which are small compared with the plasma frequency.

I. INTRODUCTION

THE characteristic modes of organized oscillation of a plasma have assumed new importance in the last few years and are again the subject of intensive investigation. Early work by Tonks and Langmuir[1] disclosed the high frequency electron oscillations in which the positive ions had little effect except to preserve over all electrical neutrality. This is, of course, but one of a number of modes in which a plasma can oscillate. The frequency of these oscillations was shown to be

$$\omega_p = (n_0 e^2 / \epsilon_0 m)^{\frac{1}{2}}, \qquad (1)$$

* This work was supported in part by the Office of Naval Research. This paper is based partially on a thesis submitted in June, 1958, by one of the authors, Mr. Trivelpiece, to the California Institute of Technology in partial fulfillment of the requirements for the Ph.D. degree.

† Now at the University of California, Berkeley, California.
[1] L. Tonks and I. Langmuir, Phys. Rev. 33, 195 (1929), L. Tonks, *ibid.* 37, 1458 (1931); *ibid.* 38, 1219 (1931).

in case the electrical fields remained entirely within the plasma, or some fraction of ω_p when some of the field extended outside the plasma. These oscillations have subsequently been investigated in considerable detail.[2] Hahn[3] and Ramo[4] have investigated the closely related problem of space charge waves of drifting ion-neutralized electron beams. To an observer moving with the average electron velocity these space charge waves appear as electron oscillations similar to those described by Tonks and Langmuir. The propagation of space charge disturbances in electron beams is largely due to the drift velocity of the electrons but, as we show below, propagation can also take place in the absence of a drift velocity (and also in the absence of thermal velocities of the electrons) when the plasma has a finite cross section.

The problem we discuss below is the nature of plasma oscillations or, since the oscillations can be thought of as waves, space charge waves of a cylindrical plasma column shown in Fig. 1, which partially fill a perfectly conducting cylinder. A steady axial magnetic field, B_0, is assumed for the sake of generality. Some of the results presented here are contained within the analyses of Hahn[3] and Ramo,[4] although the latter make no specific reference to stationary plasmas. Propagation of electromagnetic waves in a wave guide partially filled with a plasma has also been investigated extensively.[5] There, attention has been focused on the effect of the plasma upon the wave-guide modes and the existence of the space charge modes of the plasma column was not recognized. These space charge modes are electromechanical in nature and can propagate at frequencies well below the wave-guide cutoff frequency and at phase velocities which can be much less than the velocity of light.[6] A considerable simplification results

[2] See, for example, D. Bohm and E. P. Gross, Phys. Rev. 75, 1851 (1949) or N. G. Van Kampen, Physica 23, 641 (1957).

[3] W. C. Hahn, Gen. Elec. Rev. 42, 258 (1939).

[4] S. Ramo, Phys. Rev. 56, 276 (1939).

[5] A. VanTrier, Appl. Sci. Research B3, 305 (1954); H. Gamo, J. Phys. Soc. Japan 8, 176 (1953). H. Suhl and L. R. Walker, Bell System Tech. J. 33, 579 (1954); 33, 939 (1954); 33, 1133 (1954).

[6] The existence of these modes has been recognized independently by others, see L. D. Smullin and P. Chorney, Proc. Inst. Radio Engrs. 46, 360 (1958), and also, Proc. Poly. Inst. of Brooklyn Symposium, April, 1958; W. O. Schumann, Z. angew. Phys. 8, 482 (1956); G. Bittner, Z. angew. Phys. 10, 117 (1958); I. B. Fainberg, CERN Symposium on High Energy Accelerators (1956); J. Dawson and C. Oberman, Phys. Fluids 2, 103 (1959).

in this case, since the electric fields are quasi-static and can be derived from a scalar potential. In Secs. III and IV of this paper we present solutions for the case of zero and infinite magnetic field in which retardation effects are not neglected.

Throughout the discussion small sinusoidal perturbations from steady state are assumed; hence we write

$$\mathbf{E}(\mathbf{r},t) = \mathbf{E}_0(\mathbf{r}) + \mathbf{E}_1(\mathbf{r})e^{j\omega t}$$
$$\rho(\mathbf{r},t) = \rho_0(\mathbf{r}) + \rho_1 e^{j\omega t} \tag{2}$$

etc., where quantities with the subscript one are complex numbers and denote the magnitude and phase of the sinusoidal perturbations. When electron thermal velocities are neglected it is appropriate to specify the properties of the plasma by giving the dielectric tensor relating the displacement to the electric field ($\mathbf{D} = \epsilon \cdot \mathbf{E}$)

$$\epsilon = \begin{bmatrix} \epsilon_1 & j\epsilon_2 & 0 \\ -j\epsilon_2 & \epsilon_1 & 0 \\ 0 & 0 & \epsilon_3 \end{bmatrix}. \tag{3}$$

When ion motion and electron collisions are neglected, ϵ_1, ϵ_2, and ϵ_3 are given by

$$\epsilon_1 = \epsilon_0 \left[1 - \frac{\omega_p^2}{\omega^2 - \omega_c^2} \right]$$

$$\epsilon_2 = \epsilon_0 \left[\frac{-\omega_p^2 \omega_c}{\omega(\omega^2 - \omega_c^2)} \right] \tag{4}$$

$$\epsilon_3 = \epsilon_0 \left[1 - \frac{\omega_p^2}{\omega^2} \right],$$

where $\omega_c = eB_0/m$ is the electron cyclotron frequency. Later we discuss the effect of collisions.

II. DISPERSION RELATION IN THE QUASI-STATIC APPROXIMATION

In the limit of slow waves, retardation effects can be neglected and it is permissible to calculate the electric fields from a scalar potential

$$\mathbf{E}_1 = -\nabla\phi_1 \tag{5}$$

and neglect the ac magnetic fields entirely. When the plasma is regarded as a dielectric there is no *free* charge hence

$$\nabla \cdot \mathbf{D}_1 = \nabla \cdot (\epsilon \cdot \mathbf{E}_1) = 0. \qquad (6)$$

By using (3) and (5) we obtain the differential equation for the potential

$$\epsilon_1 \left[\frac{1}{r} \frac{\partial}{\partial r} \left(r \frac{\partial \phi_1}{\partial r} \right) + \frac{1}{r^2} \frac{\partial^2 \phi_1}{\partial \theta^2} \right] + \epsilon_3 \frac{\partial^2 \phi_1}{\partial z^2} = 0, \qquad (7)$$

which has as a suitable solution (including the axis)

$$\phi_1 = A J_n(Tr) e^{-j(n\theta + \beta z)} \quad 0 < r < a, \qquad (8)$$

where

$$T^2 = -\beta^2 \frac{\epsilon_3}{\epsilon_1} = -\beta^2 \left[\frac{(\omega^2 - \omega_p^2)(\omega^2 - \omega_c^2)}{\omega^2(\omega^2 - \omega_p^2 - \omega_c^2)} \right]. \qquad (9)$$

This solution is valid inside the plasma. Outside the plasma $(a < r < b)$, a solution of Laplace's which vanishes at the perfectly conducting surface $(r = b)$ is required

$$\phi_1 = B[I_n(\beta r) K_n(\beta b) - I_n(\beta b) K_n(\beta r)] e^{-j(n\theta + \beta z)}. \qquad (10)$$

At the boundary of the plasma $(r = a)$ normal displacement and tangential electric field must be continuous. This leads to two relations between the constants A and B which are satisfied only if

$$\epsilon_1 T a \frac{J_n'(Ta)}{J_n(Ta)} + n\epsilon_2$$

$$= K_e \epsilon_0 \beta a \frac{I_n'(\beta a) K_n(\beta b) - I_n(\beta b) K_n'(\beta a)}{I_n(\beta a) K_n(\beta b) - I_n(\beta b) K_n(\beta a)}, \qquad (11)$$

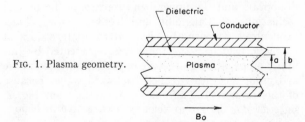

FIG. 1. Plasma geometry.

where K_e is the dielectric constant of the region outside the plasma. Equation (11) is the dispersion relation determining ω when β is given or β when ω is given.

Plasma Filling the Conducting Cylinder

When the plasma completely fills the wave guide $(a=b)$, the potential given by (8) must vanish at $r=a$, hence $J_n(Ta)=0$ or $Ta=p_{n\nu}$ where $p_{n\nu}$ is the νth zero of the nth order Bessel function. Solving (9) for the propagation constant

$$\beta a = \pm p_{n\nu} \left[\frac{-\omega^2(\omega^2-\omega_p^2-\omega_c^2)}{(\omega^2-\omega_p^2)(\omega^2-\omega_c^2)} \right]^{\frac{1}{2}}. \qquad (12)$$

For each set of integers, n and ν there are two waves whose propagation constants are given by (12). The potential functions corresponding to these waves form a complete orthogonal set at a plane $z=$ constant and they can be superposed to represent an arbitrary disturbance. The normalized phase characteristics (ω vs β) obtained from Eq. (12) are shown in Fig. 2 for a strong magnetic field ($\omega_c > \omega_p$) and for a weak magnetic field ($\omega_c < \omega_p$). In both cases there are two propagation bands (β real) and two bands of no propagation (β imaginary; evanescent waves). The limits of these bands are given by the poles and zeros of (12) and are indicated in Fig. 2. When ω^2 is much less than both ω_p^2 and ω_c^2, the phase velocity is nearly a constant equal to

$$v_p = \frac{a}{p_{n\nu}} \frac{\omega_p\omega_c}{(\omega_p^2+\omega_c^2)^{\frac{1}{2}}}. \qquad (13)$$

In the limit of zero magnetic field the lower band disappears and the upper band represents the plasma oscillations of Langmuir and Tonks ($\omega=\omega_p$, independent of wavelength). For intermediate values of magnetic field ($\omega_c \sim \omega_p$) the waves represented by this upper propagation band have oppositely directed phase and group velocities (called backward waves because of this property). This fact is apparent from Fig. 2, since $d\omega/d\beta$, the group velocity, is negative in regions where ω/β, the phase velocity, is positive.

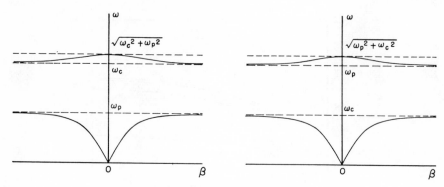

FIG. 2. Phase characteristics of a plasma filled wave guide (quasi-static approximation). Frequency *versus* axial propagation constant for $b=a$.

Plasma Partially Filling the Conducting Cylinder

In this case Eq. (11), together with the auxilliary relation (9), must be solved. It is no longer possible to describe modes of different angular and radial variation with a universal relation such as (12). We have investigated the character of the waves by solving (9) and (11) for some representative situations. The phase characteristics of the lowest mode (smallest Ta value) with no angular dependence is shown in Fig. 3. The principal difference from the results of Fig. 2 is that when $\omega_c < \omega_p$, the upper cutoff frequency (the frequency for which $\beta a \to \infty$) of the lower branch is no longer ω_c, but is instead, $\omega_p/(1+K_e)^{\frac{1}{2}}$. Modes with larger Ta values (corresponding to $\nu = 2, 3, \cdots$) do not have this property, however, their upper cutoff frequency is still given by ω_c. Thus as the magnetic field is reduced to zero, there remains only *one* circularly symmetric mode which propagates at low frequencies.

The nature of this mode can be understood in the following way. Oppositely directed traveling waves combine to produce a standing wave in which the plasma simply oscillates sinusoidally with frequency ω. The electric field configuration is shown in Fig. 4 at a time when it is a maximum. Electrons are displaced so that the electronic charge and ionic charge continue

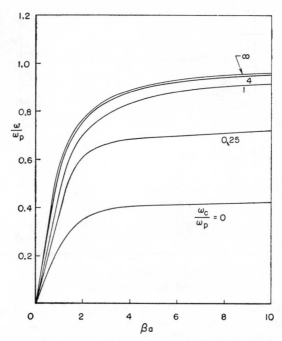

Fig. 3. Phase characteristics of a plasma filled wave guide (quasi-static approximation). Frequency *versus* axial propagation constant for $b=2a$, $K_e=4.0$.

to balance in the interior of the plasma but the deformation of the surface bounding the electrons results in the "surface charge" layer shown. Under the action of the electric field, the electrons in the interior of the plasma will tend to be restored to their equilibrium position. The restoring force is weaker for long wavelength (small β) perturbations than for short wavelength (large β) perturbations. The mass of electrons which must be moved is also larger for long wavelength perturbation, hence the oscillation frequency is clearly lower than for short wavelength perturbations. This accounts qualitatively for the frequency-wavelength characteristic of Fig. 3. The fact that ω depends on β implies a finite group velocity and hence a propagation of energy. Although we have, as an approximation, neglected the ac magnetic field, it is clear that the energy transport is actually by the electromagnetic field (Poynting vector) since, on the average, the plasma remains at rest.

III. PLASMA FILLED CYLINDRICAL WAVE GUIDE IN AN INFINITE AXIAL MAGNETIC FIELD

In the limit of large magnetic field, the dyadic permittivity (3) reduces to a form where the E modes and the H modes[7] are uncoupled and Maxwell's equations are readily solved exactly. The H modes will not be considered since they are not perturbed by the presence of the plasma. Assuming wave solutions $\exp[j(\omega t - \beta z)]$ we have for the E modes

$$\nabla_T^2 E_{1z} + \{(k^2 - \beta^2)[1 - (\omega_p^2/\omega^2)]\} E_{1z} = 0, \quad (14)$$

where ∇_T^2 is the transverse Laplacian operator and $k = \omega/c$. If we

$$T^2 = (k^2 - \beta^2)[1 - (\omega_p^2/\omega^2)], \quad (15)$$

the solution of (14) that is finite on the axis is

$$E_{1z}(r,\theta,z,t) = A J_n(Tr) e^{j(\omega t - n\theta - \beta z)}. \quad (16)$$

The boundary condition at the wave-guide surface $(r = a)$ requires that $J_n(Ta) = 0$; hence $Ta = p_{n\nu}$. Solving (15) explicitly for the propagation constant we have

$$(\beta a)^2 = (ka)^2 - \frac{p_{n\nu}^2}{1 - (\omega_p^2/\omega^2)}. \quad (17)$$

The phase characteristics (ω vs β) for (17) are shown in Fig. 5. The upper pass band represents the electromagnetic wave-guide modes which are perturbed by the presence of the plasma. The lower propagation band extends from $\omega = 0$ to $\omega = \omega_p$ and represents the space charge wave. When the plasma frequency is small compared with the empty wave-guide cutoff frequency, the space charge waves have phase velocities much less than the velocity of light.

To establish the effect of retardation we set $\omega_c = \infty$ in Eq. (12) obtaining

$$(\beta a)^2 = -\frac{p_{n\nu}^2}{[1 - (\omega_p^2/\omega^2)]}.$$

Comparing this with (17), we see that the static-approximation is valid if

[7] S. Ramo and J. Whinnery, *Fields and Waves in Modern Radio* (John Wiley & Sons, Inc., New York, 1953), second edition, Chap. 8.

$$(\omega_p a/c)^2 \ll p_{n\nu}^2$$

which is precisely the condition that the square of the low-frequency phase velocity be much less than c^2.

The space charge wave propagation in the lower pass band can be understood in an approximate way using the longitudinal and transverse components of

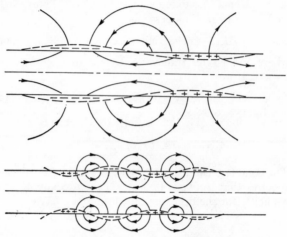

FIG. 4. Electric field configuration at the time of maximum field for a circularly symmetric surface wave.

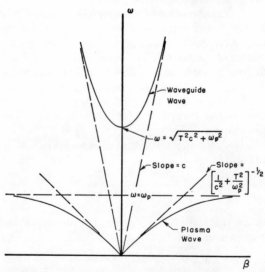

FIG. 5. Phase characteristics of a plasma filled wave guide for infinite axial magnetic field.

the permittivity

$$(j\omega D_{1z}/E_{1z}) = j\omega\epsilon_L = j\omega\epsilon_0(1-\omega_p{}^2/\omega^2)$$
$$(j\omega D_{1r}/E_{1r}) = j\omega\epsilon_T = j\omega\epsilon_0. \tag{18}$$

These quantities are the displacement current to electric field ratio and in this case approximately represent the longitudinal and transverse susceptance per unit length of the plasma-filled wave guide. The equivalent electrical transmission line suggested by these susceptances is shown in Fig. 6 and has similar propagation characteristics to those depicted by the lower branch of Fig. 5. A slight extension of this notion permits the qualitative investigation of space charge waves for finite magnetic fields when the plasma does not completely fill the wave guide.

The nonzero slope of the space charge wave phase characteristics implies a real power flow associated with these waves. The time average z-directed power flow for the lowest mode of axial symmetry is obtained by integrating Poynting's vector over the wave-guide cross section. The result of this calculation is

$$\bar{P}_z = \epsilon_0(\pi a^2/2)[\omega\beta/(k^2-\beta^2)^2]E_{1z}{}^2(0)(p_{01})^2 J_1(p_{01}). \tag{19}$$

The power flow can also be computed by multiplying the sum of the time average stored electric, magnetic and kinetic energies by the group velocity $(\partial\omega/\partial\beta)$ of the wave.

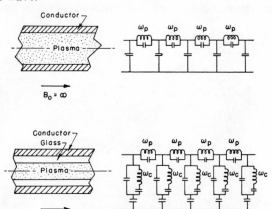

FIG. 6. Equivalent transmission line for plasma filled wave guide with infinite axial magnetic field.

IV. ZERO MAGNETIC FIELD

In this section we show the effect of retardation in the absence of a dc magnetic field. Following the method of reference 7, we can write the E-mode solution for circularly symmetric waves which have phase velocity less than the velocity of light $(\beta^2 > \omega^2/c^2)$ as

$$E_{1z} = A[I_0(\gamma r)/I_0(\gamma a)]\exp[j(\omega t - \beta z)] \quad r < a \qquad (20)$$

$$= A\frac{I_0(\gamma_0 r)K_0(\gamma_0 b) - I_0(\gamma_0 b)K_0(\gamma_0 r)}{I_0(\gamma_0 a)K_0(\gamma_0 b) - I_0(\gamma_0 b)K_0(\gamma_0 a)}$$

$$\times \exp[j(\omega t - \beta z)], \quad a < r < b \quad (21)$$

where

$$\gamma_0^2 = \beta^2 - \omega^2/c^2 \qquad (22)$$

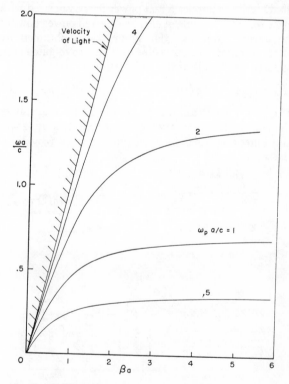

Fig. 7. Phase characteristics for no axial magnetic field $(b/a = \infty)$ from Eq. (24).

and

$$\gamma^2 = \beta^2 - (\omega^2 - \omega_p^2/c^2) = \gamma_0^2 + \omega_p^2/c^2. \qquad (23)$$

This solution has been chosen so that E_{1z} is finite on the axis, continuous at plasma boundary $(r=a)$ and zero at the metallic boundary $(r=b)$. The tangential magnetic field $(H_{1\theta})$ must also be continuous at the plasma boundary. Imposing this condition leads to the determinantal relation

$$\left(1 - \frac{\omega_p^2}{\omega^2}\right)\frac{I_0'(\gamma a)}{\gamma a I_0(\gamma a)}$$
$$= \frac{1}{\gamma_0 a}\left[\frac{I_0'(\gamma_0 a)K_0(\gamma_0 b) - I_0(\gamma_0 b)K'_0(\gamma_0 a)}{I_0(\gamma_0 a)K_0(\gamma_0 b) - I_0(\gamma_0 b)K_0(\gamma_0 a)}\right]. \qquad (24)$$

Each component of the field is largest at the plasma boundary and decreases away from the boundary. Outside the plasma the rate of decrease is that which is characteristic of any slow wave $(\gamma_0^2 = \beta^2 - \omega^2/c^2)$. Inside the plasma the rate of decrease is larger than outside $(\gamma^2 > \gamma_0^2)$ and the extra contribution to $\gamma^2(\omega_p^2/c^2)$ is characteristic of the plasma penetration problem (the low frequency penetration depth in a lossless plasma is $d = c/\omega_p$). When $(\omega_p a/c)^2 \ll 1$, Eq. (24) gives the same result as Eq. (11) when $\omega_c = 0$ is substituted into the latter. When $\omega_p a/c$ becomes large, the low-frequency phase velocity approaches the velocity of light as shown in Fig. 7. The fields do not penetrate appreciably into the plasma and it behaves much like a conductor. The ratio E_z/E_r outside the plasma becomes very small and the mode goes over to the TEM mode of a coaxial line.

V. MISCELLANEOUS TOPICS

Faraday Rotation

The phenomenon of Faraday rotation was an important consideration in the analysis of the perturbation of wave-guide modes[5] by the plasma and it is of interest to see if the angular dependent space charge wave modes have the same property. A superposition of the $n = +1$ and $n = -1$ modes yields a composite wave in which the transverse field has a certain angle of polarization, and if these modes have different phase veloci-

ties, the polarization angle of the composite field rotates
as the waves propagate down the wave guide. Higher
order angular dependent modes may exhibit an analogous effect.

When the plasma fills the wave guide, modes having
equal and opposite values of n have the same phase
velocity and thus there will be no rotation of the plane
of polarization. However, when the plasma does not
completely fill the wave guide, the propagation equation (11) contains a term which is an odd function of n
and modes of opposite sign of n may have different phase
velocities thus giving rise to Faraday rotation. The
phase characteristics for the $n = \pm 1$ modes of lowest
radial order are shown in Fig. 8. The lower branches
are the modes which involve interior space charge
bunching (body waves) and the upper branches are the
$n = \pm 1$ surface wave modes which have been split by
the magnetic field and exhibit Faraday rotation only
for small magnetic fields, where the splitting is not too
large. For typical plasmas and magnetic fields available
in the laboratory, 360° rotation of the plane of polarization in an axial distance of 5 cm at 500 Mc is theoretically possible.

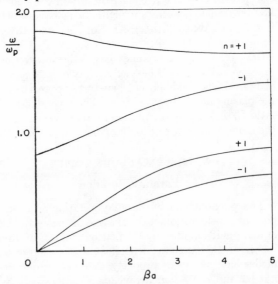

FIG. 8. Phase characteristics of the $n = \pm 1$ angular dependent
modes (quasi-static approximation), for $b/a = 2$, $K_e = 1$,
$\omega_p/\omega_c = 2.0$.

Space Charge Waves in Drifting Plasmas

The space charge waves in stationary plasma columns are closely related to the space charge waves associated with the drifting motion of an electron beam[3,4] and the solutions already found are easily modified by means of a nonrelativistic coordinate transformation to include a uniform drift velocity along the axis of symmetry. If ω and β are the frequency and propagation constant in the coordinate system where the electrons are at rest, the frequency ω' and the propagation constant β' in a coordinate system where the electrons drift with velocity u_0 are

$$\omega' = \omega + \beta u_0, \tag{25}$$

$$\beta' = \beta. \tag{26}$$

Wavelengths in the two systems are the same and ω' is the Doppler shifted frequency. Figure 9 is a typical ω-β diagram for the plasma-filled wave guide in an infinite axial magnetic field where the plasma has a uniform drift velocity u_0. This diagram has been constructed from the lower branch of Fig. 5 with the aid of Eqs. (25) and (26). The slanted dashed lines represent the one-dimensional space charge waves in an electron beam of infinite radius.

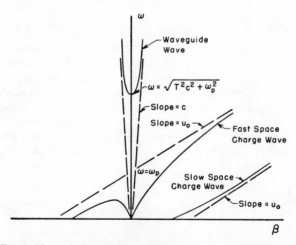

FIG. 9. Phase characteristics of space charge waves of a drifting plasma or electron beam in an infinite axial magnetic field.

In addition to the usual slow and fast space charge wave there are two additional waves of negative propagation constant below the plasma frequency. For these waves to exist, the electron drift velocity must be less than the asymptotic low frequency phase velocity in the system where the electrons are at rest. This requirement can be expressed (for the case of infinite magnetic field)

$$\omega_p a/u_0 p_{n\nu} > 1 \quad \text{or} \quad \omega_p a/u_0 > 2.405.$$

The latter form applies for the lowest mode when the electron beam fills the conducting cylinder and leads to the conclusion that the perveance $(P=I_0/V_0^{\frac{3}{2}})$ must be greater than about 200×10^{-6}. Thus a one milliampere electron beam of less than 3-v potential can propagate four waves at frequencies well below the plasma frequency instead of the usual two.[8] These additional waves may be of importance in investigating how noise disturbances propagate from the potential minimum of a diode used in a microwave tube when the potential minimum plasma frequency is greater than the operating frequency of the tube.

Attenuation of Space Charge Waves by Electron Collisions

In a plasma produced by an electrical discharge the electrons will have collisions with the positive ions, the neutral gas molecules and the walls of the container. These collisions interrupt the electron-wave interaction and remove energy from the wave. The resulting attenuation of the wave can be investigated approximately in the case of zero magnetic field by defining an average electron collision frequency ν_c and replacing ω by $\omega - j\nu_c/2$ in the equations for the propagation constant. An approximate solution to these equations is obtained by writing

$$\alpha(\omega,\nu_c) + j\beta(\omega,\nu_c)$$
$$= j\beta(\omega,0) + j[\partial\beta(\omega,0)/\partial\omega][-j\nu_c/2] + \cdots. \quad (27)$$

---

[8] R. W. Gould and A. W. Trivelpiece, "A new mode of wave propagation on electron beams," Proceedings of the 1958 Symposium on Electronic Waveguides, Polytechnic Institute of Brooklyn.

When ν_c is small, the first two terms give a satisfactory approximation

$$\alpha(\omega,\nu_c) = [\partial\beta(\omega,0)/\partial\omega]\nu_c/2. \qquad (28)$$

$$\beta(\omega,\nu_c) = \beta(\omega,0). \qquad (29)$$

Thus to a first approximation the propagation constant is unaffected by collisions and the attenuation is proportional to the collision frequency and inversely proportional to the group velocity of the wave.

VI. EXPERIMENTAL RESULTS

Description of Experiment

To experimentally investigate space charge wave propagation in plasmas, the wavelength and signal strength of waves along a plasma column were measured using the apparatus shown schematically in Fig. 10. The plasma is the positive column of a low pressure mercury arc discharge. The radio-frequency signal is introduced on the discharge anode and is sampled by means of a movable probe which is inserted in the slotted cylindrical wave guide that surrounds the plasma column. The pertinent dimensions of the apparatus are given in Table I, together with the range of parameters over which propagation was investigated. The pressure of the mercury vapor within the discharge tube is controlled by regulating the temperature of a mercury reservoir which is attached to the tube (not shown in Fig. 10). In order to obtain precise experi-

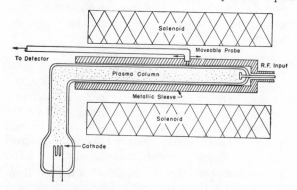

Fig. 10. Schematic of apparatus to measure phase and attenuation characteristics of space charge waves in a plasma.

TABLE I. Pertinent dimensions of experimental apparatus used in space charge wave propagation experiment.

Diameter of plasma	0.328 in.
Diameter of tube containing plasma	0.410 in.
Diameter of slotted wave guide	0.410 and 0.750 in.
Length of plasma column	25 cm
Signal frequency range	10 to 4000 mc
Cyclotron frequency range	0 to 5000 mc
Plasma frequency range	500 to 5000 mc
Temperature of mercury in tube	$300\pm0.1°$K
Empty wave guide cutoff frequency (approx)	25 000 mc
Pressure of mercury at 300°K (approx)	2 microns
Mean free path of plasma electrons (approx)	5 cm

mental data, it is desirable to immerse the entire discharge apparatus in a thermostatic bath; however, the mechanical problems involved discouraged this. When only the temperature of the reservoir was regulated the results were reproducible.

The wavelengths were measured using two techniques. The first was to measure the distance between nulls of the standing wave pattern that resulted from the energy reflected from the unterminated end of the plasma wave guide when there was sufficient reflected signal to permit this. The second, used when the reflected signal was negligible, was to compare the phase of the traveling wave on the plasma column with a reference signal from the generator and measure the distance for a phase shift of 2π. (This is just the distance between nulls when the reference signal and the sampled signal are adjusted to the same amplitude.) The first technique is useful for a long wavelength lowloss situation and the second for a short wavelength high-loss situation.

Finite Magnetic Field

Figure 11 shows the measured and theoretical values of propagation constant $(\beta=2\pi/\lambda)$ for several different values of discharge current and magnetic field for the case where the conducting cylinder tightly fits the glass discharge tube. It is convenient to normalize the signal frequency ω to the cyclotron frequency since the latter is known from the magnet current. Plotting the theoretical results in this way gives a family of curves, each curve for a different ratio ω_p/ω_c. The theoretical curve

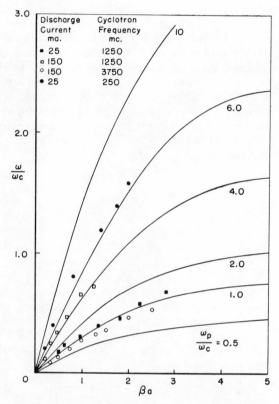

FIG. 11. Theoretical and measured phase characteristics of plasma space charge waves for $b/a = 1.2$, $K_e = 4.6$.

which best fits the experimental data, when the latter is plotted in terms of the same variables, gives a direct measure of ω_p/ω_c and hence ω_p, the plasma frequency.

The backward wave pass bands are not shown in Fig. 11 since it was not possible to observe transmission in this mode with a tightly fitting metallic conductor. The electric field outside the plasma is very weak for this mode and our traveling probe is coupled only very weakly to the field since at most it is flush with the surrounding cylinder. In order to couple the probe more strongly to the fields, a conducting cylinder whose inner diameter was approximately twice the outer diameter of the glass tube was used and the sampling probe allowed to extend in to the glass. In this manner it was possible to obtain transmission in this mode, although wavelength measurements were difficult because of the large attenuation and a high noise level. Figure 12 shows results for this mode together with measurements made in the forward wave mode for the same experimental conditions. Also shown are theoretical curves for $\omega_p/\omega_c = 2.0$ (solid curve) and $\omega_p/\omega_c = 1.9$ (dashed curve). The experimental points are in good agreement with the theoretical curve for $\omega_p/\omega_c = 1.9$. (The forward wave characteristics are relatively insensitive to small changes in ω_p/ω_c hence the curves for $\omega_p/\omega_c = 1.9$ and $\omega_p/\omega_c = 2.0$ nearly coincide.)

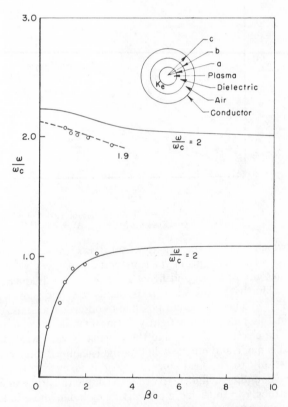

FIG. 12. Theoretical and measured phase characteristics of plasma space charge waves illustrating the upper pass band (backward wave), for $b/a = 1.2$, $c/b = 2.0$, $K_e = 4.6$. Discharge current of 5 ma and cyclotron frequency of 250 mc.

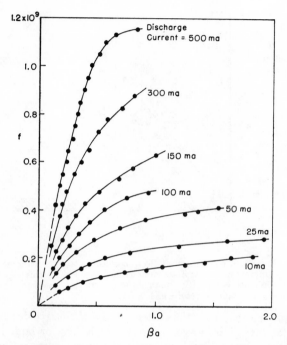

FIG. 13. Measured phase characteristics of plasma space charge waves for no magnetic field for $a=0.52$ cm, $b=0.62$ cm, $K=4.6$.

Zero Magnetic Field

In the absence of a steady magnetic field there is no interior space charge bunching and the waves are in the nature of surface waves (Fig. 4). Experimental points for different discharge currents are shown in Fig. 13. The various curves are approximately similar except for a change in the vertical scale due to the different plasma frequency in each case. In a low pressure mercury the electron density, hence ω_p^2, is proportional to the discharge current (Fig. 14).

When the experimental results are compared with the theoretical ω-β curves there appears to be a systematic discrepancy; for values of βa greater than unity the observed frequency is generally too low. This departure of the experimental data from the theoretical behavior is probably attributable to the variation of average charge density (ρ_0) with radius. For large βa the fields are very much stronger near the surface of the

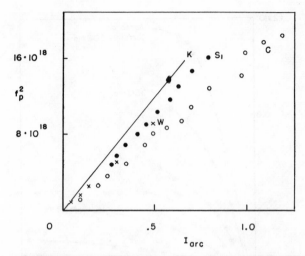

Fig. 14. A comparison of electron density measurements made by different methods: W = space charge wave method (this paper), C = microwave cavity method, S = scattering method, and K = semi-empirical results of Klarfeld.

plasma than near the center. Thus the effective density (as far as the wave is concerned) is less for large βa than for small βa, hence the droop in the curve. It has furthermore been shown theoretically that the low frequency phase velocity is proportional to the *average*‡ charge density, i.e.,

$$v_p = \lim_{\beta a \to 0} \frac{\omega}{\beta} = \left[\left(\langle \omega_p{}^2 \rangle a^2 \ln\frac{b}{a} \right)^{\frac{1}{2}} \Big/ 2K_e \right].$$

Thus a measurement of the low frequency phase velocity provides a means of measuring average electron density.

Plasma Diagnostics

The usual methods of diagnosing low density plasmas such as cavity perturbation or electromagnetic transmission, require signal source frequencies higher than the plasma frequency, and for very dense plasmas the frequencies required are so high that the experimental techniques become rather difficult. However, space charge waves usually propagate below the plasma frequency, and for plasmas with low collision frequencies,

---

‡ Averaged over the cross section of the column.

the phase characteristics of these space charge waves
depend only on the geometry, the magnetic field, and
the charge density. The geometry and magnetic field
are known so that an experimental measurement of
the wavelength of the wave may be used to measure the
charge density.

The results of charge density measurements for
various discharge currents and magnetic fields are
shown in Fig. 15. An enhancement of charge density as
the magnetic field is increased is observed. The mean
free path of a plasma electron is much longer than the
diameter of the plasma for no magnetic field and the
plasma electrons mostly collide with the wall of the
discharge tube where they recombine. For a large

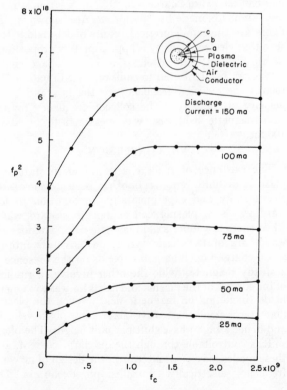

FIG. 15. Measured electron density (expressed in terms of the
plasma frequency $f_p = \omega_p/2\pi$) as a function of axial magnetic
field (expressed in terms of the electron cyclotron frequency
$f_c = \omega_c/2\pi$).

magnetic field the cyclotron diameter is much less than the diameter of the plasma and the plasma electrons no longer strike the wall of the discharge tube, but drift axially along the tube spending a greater time in the discharge before recombining, thus making the equilibrium charge density greater for a given current. The transition between these two regimes occurs at a magnetic field strength which makes the cyclotron radius for electrons equal to the plasma radius.

Boyd, Field, and Gould measured the charge density of a plasma column by microwave cavity techniques[9] and by scattering from the column in a wave guide.[10] For the same geometry and operating conditions, the charge density was measured using space charge wave technique. Figure 14 shows our measurements of charge density *versus* discharge current in relation to the measurements made by Boyd, *et al.* Also shown in this figure are the semi-empirical results of Klarfeld.[11] It is seen that electron density is approximately proportional to arc current. The attenuation of the space charge waves can be attributed to collision loss. Equation (28) relates the collision frequency to the loss and group velocity of the wave. The collision frequency for the zero magnetic field case was measured to be about 100 mc.

VII. CONCLUSION

The existence of space charge waves in stationary plasmas of finite cross section has been demonstrated theoretically and experimentally. In addition to forward waves, a plasma can support backward waves when there is a finite axial magnetic field. The forward waves are of two basic types; one involves interior space charge bunching and depends on the presence of a steady magnetic field; the other involves a rippling of the surface of the plasma and exists for weak magnetic fields (including no magnetic field). When the plasma diameter is small these waves have a low phase velocity and hence a high phase shift per unit length. The phase shift is controllable through the discharge current, and these modes may be of interest in the design of new low frequency electrically controlled phase shifters. The

[9] M. A. Biondi and S. C. Brown, Phys. Rev. **75**, 1700 (1949).
[10] Boyd, Field, and Gloud, Phys. Rev. **109**, 1393 (1958).
[11] B. Klarfeld, J. Phys. (U. S. S. R.) **5**, 155 (1941).

angular dependent modes exhibit Faraday rotation with higher rotation per unit length than generally obtained with the perturbed waveguide modes. This might make possible relatively small low frequency isolators, provided the ratio of attenuation to rotation can be made small enough.

The existence of the backward wave makes possible the design of a backward wave oscillator in which the plasma is the slow wave circuit. In generating higher microwave frequencies this shifts the emphasis from the fabrication of small and delicate slow wave circuits to that of obtaining high electron densities or large magnetic fields. Experiments to demonstrate traveling wave interaction between these modes and an electron beam are already in progress in this laboratory and preliminary results are encouraging.

Finally, the techniques discussed here must also be regarded as a new and potentially valuable plasma diagnostic tool. One immediately apparent application is the determination of electron densities by measuring the wavelength of the space charge waves which propagate on the plasma column at frequencies below the plasma frequency. The usual cavity method of measurement of electron densities is limited to densities for which the plasma frequency is less than the signal frequency. The use of space charge waves to measure electron densities thus extends the range of densities which can be measured with microwaves.

references

1. K. R. Spangenberg, Vacuum Tubes, New York: McGraw-Hill Book Co., 1948; pp. 475-526.

2. A. Arsenjewa-Heil and O. Heil, "Eine neue Methode zur Erzeugung kurzer ungedämpfter electromagnetischen Wellen von grosser Intensität" (A new method of generating short undamped electromagnetic waves of high intensity), Z. Phys. 95: 752-773, 1935.

3. R. H. Varian and S. F. Varian, "A high frequency oscillator and amplifier," J. Appl. Phys. 10: 321-327, 1939.

4. D. L. Webster, "Theory of klystron oscillations," J. Appl. Phys. 10: 864-872, 1939.

5. W. C. Hahn, "Small signal theory of velocity-modulated electron beams," Gen. Elec. Rev. 33: 591-596, 1939.

6. S. Ramo, "Space charge waves and field waves in an electron beam," Phys. Rev. 56: 276-283, 1939.

7. W. W. Rigrod and J. A. Lewis, "Wave propagation along a magnetically focused cylindrical electron beam," Bell Syst. Tech. J. 33: 399-416, 1954.

8. L. Brillouin, "A theorem of Larmor and its importance for electrons in magnetic fields," Phys. Rev. 67: 260-266, 1945.

9. G. R. Brewer, "Some effects of magnetic field strength on space-charge wave propagation," Proc. IRE 44: 896-903, 1956.

10. J. Labus, "Space charge waves along magnetically focused electron beam," Proc. IRE 45: 854-861, 1957.

11. H. Suhl and L. R. Walker, "Topics in guided wave propagation through gyromagnetic media," Bell Syst. Tech. J. 33: 579-659, 939-986, 1133-1194, 1954.

12. H. Gamo, "The Faraday rotation of waves in a circular waveguide," J. Phys. Soc. Japan 8: 176-182, 1953.

13. A. A. T. M. Van Trier, "Guided electromagnetic waves in anisotropic media," Appl. Sci. Res. B3: 305-371, 1954.

14. J. R. Pierce, Traveling-Wave Tubes, Princeton, N.J.: D. Van Nostrand, 1950.

15. J. R. Pierce and W. E. Danielson, "Minimum noise figure of traveling-wave tubes with uniform helices," J. Appl. Phys. 25: 1163-1165, 1954.

16. S. Bloom and R. W. Peter, "A minimum noise figure for the traveling-wave tube," RCA Rev. 15: 252-267, 1954.

17. F. N. H. Robinson, "Microwave shot noise in electron beams and the minimum noise factor of travelling-wave tubes and klystrons," J. Brit. IRE 42: 79-86, 1954.

18. D. A. Watkins, "Noise reduction in beam type amplifiers," Proc. IRE 40: 65-70, 1952.

19. J. R. Pierce, "General sources of noise in vacuum tubes," Trans. IRE ED-1: 135-167, 1954.

20. A. W. Trivelpiece, R. W. Gould, and L. M. Field, "Low noise preamplifiers for radio astronomy observation," California Institute of Technology (Vacuum Tube Research Project), QSR-No. 15, October 1956.

21. A. W. Trivelpiece, R. W. Gould, and L. M. Field, "Low noise preamplifiers for radio astronomy observation," California Institute of Technology (Vacuum Tube Research Project), QSR-No. 18, July 1957.

22. L. D. Smullin and P. Chorney, "Electron-stimulated ion oscillators," Massachusetts Institute of Technology (Research Laboratory for Electronics), QPR-No. 47, October 1957.

23. W. R. Smythe, Static and Dynamic Electricity, New York: McGraw-Hill Book Co., 1950; 2d ed., p. 519.

24. J. C. Slater, Microwave Electronics, Princeton, N.J.: D. Van Nostrand, 1954, pp. 169-187.

25. A. W. Trivelpiece, R. W. Gould, and R. K. Cooper, "Electromechanical modes of propagation in plasma waveguides and their application to measurement of electron density in a cylindrical plasma column," California Institute of Technology (Vacuum Tube Research Project), unpublished memorandum.

26. H. R. Johnson, "Backward-wave oscillators," Proc. IRE, 43, 684-697, 1955.

27. R. W. Gould, Course Notes on Physical Electronics, California Institute of Technology, 1956-57.

28. C. K. Birdsall, "A simple method for obtaining phase velocity, attenuation, and impedance of a sheath helix in arbitrary surroundings," Hughes Research and Development Laboratories, Culver City, Calif., Memo ETL-12, 1 July 1953.

LS